YOUR DREAM
JOB IS HERE

The Impact Technology Revolution and the New Jobs Saving the World

Darlene Damm

Darlene Damm

Cover design by: Darlene Damm
Author photo credit: Nick Otto

Library of Congress Control Number: 2024912367

ISBN 979-8-218-45109-7
ISBN 979-8-218-45108-0 (ebook)

CONTENTS

YOUR DREAM JOB IS HERE

PART I

THE END OF AN ERA

CHAPTER 1—SAY GOODBYE TO THE DEAD-END JOBS THAT ARE DESTROYING THE PLANET AND MAKING US MISERABLE

L ydia, a teacher of 20 years, is ready to quit. She became an educator to make a difference in children's lives, but today, her job is unbearable. Her kids are way behind in their coursework, their parents are fighting with each other, her principal micromanages her, her classroom has a broken air conditioner, and several of her students live in terror of school shootings. On top of that, Lydia is living paycheck-to-paycheck and was just diagnosed with diabetes.

Luis is similarly overwhelmed. He works at a ranch, hiring and managing workers, and ordering supplies. Every day he lives in fear the ranch will shut down and he'll lose his job. His town is already several years into a severe drought and the ranch is importing food and water for the cattle. Customers are buying less beef, and the numbers aren't adding up. To make matters worse, his ex-wife, Jessica moved out of state with her new boyfriend, leaving him alone to raise their four-year-old daughter, Molly. When Luis thinks about the future, he feels sick to his stomach.

Although your circumstances might be different from Lydia and Luis, given all the challenges facing our world right now, you're likely feeling many of their same emotions. Whether you're a doctor, consultant, lawyer, nurse, business leader, sales assistant, editor, pilot, accountant, restaurant worker, or simply someone stringing together multiple jobs to make ends meet, you're probably feeling a deep sense of burnout and inability to get ahead.

You're also probably sick and tired of the many social, environmental and political problems plaguing our world. Perhaps you fled your hometown because of increased crime or toxic politics. Perhaps you lost your house in a flood or forest fire. Perhaps you never could afford a house in the first place. If you grew up believing if you worked hard and did everything right, the American Dream could be yours, you're probably feeling a lot of anger, frustration and confusion right now.

Given the circumstances, I'm sure you wouldn't be surprised if I told you Lydia and Luis, like hundreds of millions of other workers, simply gave up and left the workforce during the Great Resignation, or perhaps "quiet quit," working for the paycheck while they checked out from their jobs mentally and emotionally. Or, like too many people, they slipped out of society entirely, losing their jobs, falling into depression, ill health, homelessness, addiction, or worse.

What if I told you that isn't what happened to Lydia and Luis— or what has to happen to you. Instead, Lydia and Luis's lives took a turn for the better. Lydia got a new job working remotely with an Ed Tech company where she spends her days doing what she loves—focusing on her students and helping them learn and grow. She no longer lives paycheck-to-paycheck and even made a down payment on a house. Her new manager never micromanages her and instead encourages her to bring new ideas to the table and supports her in every way possible, including taking care of her health.

As for Luis, he's working at a robotic farm managing and training new hires and purchasing equipment and supplies. He's doubled his salary, has a flexible schedule allowing him to plan his day around Molly, and no longer worries about the drought as his robotic farm uses 90% less water than a traditional farm.

How did Lydia and Luis improve their lives and jobs so dramatically at a time when everything else in the world seems to be spiraling downhill?

They found jobs working with impact technology companies,

a new type of company I've observed emerging from the Fourth Industrial Revolution. What is the Fourth Industrial Revolution? It's a term for how new technologies, like advanced computing, artificial intelligence, robotics, renewable energy, and biotechnology, are transforming companies, industries, our economy, and society. The first impact technology companies are already here, and hundreds of thousands more are coming, creating millions of high-paying, meaningful, good jobs. This new revolution, happening in every corner of the world, is changing the type of jobs available to all of us—for the better! While it might seem you will be stuck in a miserable, low-paying job for the rest of your life, and our world is spiraling downhill into crisis after crisis, a very different and better future is right around the corner.

What are impact technology companies? They're companies using breakthrough technologies such as artificial intelligence, robotics, advanced manufacturing, blockchain, biotechnology, and more to build products and services solving our world's most urgent social and environmental problems. They're working in areas such as food, agriculture, education, healthcare, clean energy, environmental restoration, biodiversity and more. They pay well, offer great benefits, and provide workers with flexibility, autonomy, and opportunities for growth. Most importantly, they're hiring now, and will need millions more workers in the future. If you get a job with one of them, you can increase your salary, work in a positive, collaborative, environment that values you, and engage in meaningful and fulfilling work making our world a better place.

While you might not have previously heard of impact technology companies, you likely have heard of some of the newly emerging industries related to them. These include new industries with abbreviated names such as "Ag Tech," which stands for "Agricultural Technology" as well as "Food Tech," "Ed Tech," "Health Tech," "Climate Tech," "Gov Tech," "Fem Tech," "Peace Tech," and more. As you may have guessed, these names refer to traditional industries people are now modernizing with new technologies. If you're working for a company in one of these industries, you might be managing a fleet of robots growing food in ways better for the environment, or using satellite data to help cities prepare for a natural disaster. You might be helping kids living in refugee camps access a world-class education through online learning and games, using artificial intelligence to create inspiring stories and films about social issues, or building electric ships, planes, and cars producing fewer emissions and pollution. You might be curing horrific diseases with data science, digitally training healthcare workers in low-income communities, or even using gigantic robots with 3D printers to build affordable housing.

While you might assume these companies only hire technologists and engineers, they hire people from all backgrounds. They need managers, salespeople, accountants, lawyers, customer service representatives, janitors, analysts, consultants and many other jobs you might be working in today. They're looking to hire you if you're a high school graduate, if you have a PhD in a highly technical subject, or if you're returning to the workforce after taking a break. They're hiring in major cities as well as remote workers in rural locations. They're hiring in the United States and almost every country around the world.

Impact technology jobs are good jobs. Many of them allow you to work from home or on hybrid schedules and offer great benefits. They pay you well, allowing you to get out of debt, and start planning for the future. They value, rather than punish you, for coming up with new ideas, taking initiative, and using your creativity and autonomy. The jobs are interesting, fun, collaborative, and bring with them tremendous opportunities for learning and growth.

How are these companies able to pay and treat you so well? Hard, tedious, and boring labor is outsourced to software, artificial intelligence, and robots, allowing you to use your creativity and imagination to solve problems, collaborate with colleagues, grow the business, and plan for the future. Today's technologies are incredibly powerful and efficient. Some computers can do decades of work in a few seconds, and robots can work 24 hours per day without rest. This means impact technology companies can generate significant amounts of revenue. While traditional companies might only keep profits for business owners and investors, impact technology companies understand if they want to be competitive in today's world, they must invest money back into their company by paying their employees well and offering their products and services to their customers at an affordable price. Because digital products and services can be sold to billions of people around the world via the Internet, some impact technology companies will grow and scale fast. This means if they want to compete, they must invest in their employee's growth and development, and continually give them more responsibility. Impact technology companies view their employees not as cogs in a wheel to be ordered around, micromanaged, and told what to do (that's for the robots), but as empowered team members and partners, helping to grow the company and take its success to the next level.

Impact technology companies are also different from traditional companies because they sell products and services solving the world's social and environmental problems, rather than products and services creating the world's social and environmental problems. If you're working in a job today, you grew up working for a company or organization that came out of the Industrial Era—the one that started in the late 1700s. The Industrial Era, while responsible for building modern society by harnessing the power of new machinery and factories, was built on an economic model of extracting as much value as possible from human workers and the planet. The goal was to pay workers as little as possible, while working them as hard as possible, and heavily managing and controlling them to do their work perfectly. Industrial Era companies also competed with one another to harvest the Earth's free natural resources as quickly as possible through logging, mining, overfishing, overfarming, and, to save costs, by dumping their pollution and waste into the water and air. While the Industrial Era provided us with the modern society we live in and benefit from today, it came at a tremendous cost: it burned out our planet and our workforce.

Now, because of recent technological breakthroughs, the tables are turning. While companies previously made profits by taking advantage of workers and the environment, impact technology companies make profits by taking advantage of technology, often to heal society and repair our planet. We're even starting to see companies with some of the highest financial valuations now building some of the world's most important social and environmental products. Perhaps one day, the people and companies who solve the most challenging social and environmental problems will also be the highest paid and most profitable.

Consider the company, NVIDIA, which builds and sells advanced computer chips and software allowing other companies to use artificial intelligence. In the middle of 2024, they made over $60 billion in revenue and reached a $3 trillion market capitalization. Despite being one of the most lucrative companies to ever exist, they're building and selling several products solving social and environmental challenges. One of their products, Ominiverse, allows customers to build digital twins or realistic digital simulations of anything from factories to replicas of human hearts. These simulations can even be connected to the physical world through sensors, tracking changes in real time. Scientists might use them to simulate how a patient might respond to heart surgery or a new type of medical device. A factory owner might use them to improve production, increase worker safety, save money, or reduce their environmental footprint. NVIDIA is also building a digital twin of the entire planet called Earth-2. This digital twin lets governments, organizations, and businesses understand, predict, and respond to climate change, water supplies, food supplies, weather, natural disasters, pollution, natural resources and more. While historically data centers have used a lot of energy to do such work, NVIDIA is also prioritizing energy efficiency, increasing efficiency by five times in some situations.

NVIDIA is one of many companies doing meaningful work while also making a profit. I mention profit not because money and greed should drive the world, but because profits allow businesses to innovate and pay their workers well. We can't save the world by driving more people into poverty, or excluding people from low-income backgrounds from working in social impact, who arguably may be the most qualified to do so. We also need companies and organizations to have access to the financial resources necessary for developing and scaling the most promising solutions, potentially to billions of people.

Today, because of technological breakthroughs, there are also now hundreds of Ed Tech, Health Tech, Food Tech and Climate Tech "unicorn companies," valued over a billion dollars each. These companies pay their employees well, and because employees often hold stock in their companies, they might have an even bigger payout if the company goes public or sells. Many impact technology companies in developed economies pay their employees six-figure salaries, as well as provide equity, benefits, and educational opportunities. While impact technology companies in lower-income economies pay less, they usually pay equal to or better than other companies in their region. Some jobs with certain impact technology companies pay extremely well. For example, the CEOs of several electric vehicle companies have compensation packages reaching half a billion dollars (with at least one CEO set to receive about $47 billion in stock.) While those CEOs are rare examples, the point is workers today no longer have to choose between doing good and paying their own bills. We live in a world where you can now do both, and there are a lot of different levels of salaries depending on your specific circumstances, preferences, and needs.

It's my aim to convince you that you no longer have to stay in a low-paying, dead-end job that is destroying the planet and exploiting your time and efforts. Instead, you can join the impact technology revolution and get a job with a company that will pay you well, value your contributions, and let you solve some of our world's most urgent social and environmental challenges. In addition to helping you understand what types of jobs are available, I promise to help you understand how to make the transition, regardless of where you are in your life and career at this moment.

Over the last 15 years, I've worked at the intersection of technology and social impact, helping pioneer the impact technology field. I've founded impact technology companies myself, and, through my work at Singularity University, an institution set up to apply advanced technologies to solve massive social challenges, taught and mentored thousands of founders and executives from around the world who went on to start impact technology companies or transform their existing Industrial Era businesses into impact technology companies. I've also worked with many international humanitarian organizations and nonprofits taking steps to modernize their operations with new technologies and business models.

Unfortunately, while impact technology workers know about these jobs, the average worker has never heard of them. In addition, most people assume only engineers or folks from Silicon Valley can work for technology companies, and if you want to save the world, you can only work for a nonprofit. These assumptions are no longer true. You need to have access to the latest knowledge about these jobs and trends to improve your own life and prospects, and together, millions of us can take on these jobs and solve the many social and environmental problems plaguing our daily lives and making us miserable.

Imagine working in a job you love with colleagues that value you. Imagine a paycheck that covers your bills and allows you to plan for the future. Imagine a world without hunger, climate change, disease, poverty, violence, crime, pollution, corruption, racism, drought, or even car accidents. This is possible through the impact technology revolution, and you can be a part of ushering in this new reality.

Chapter by chapter, I'll walk you through the new impact technology industries, companies, and jobs available to you. I'll help you understand what the Fourth Industrial Revolution is, and the various breakthrough technologies involved, such as artificial intelligence, robotics, blockchain, advanced manufacturing, and biotechnology. We'll discuss how these technologies allow companies to solve social problems, while also being profitable and treating their workers well, and why this sector is poised for growth.

Together, we'll do deep dives into sectors including Ag Tech, Food Tech, Climate Tech, Health Tech, Ed Tech and more. I'll share the skills you will need and not need to secure jobs in these industries, and why you likely already have many of the skills employers are seeking. I'll help you think through risks and opportunities in these industries and assess your readiness to make a change. I'll help you transition into your new job at your own pace by sharing three pathways to success: learn, experiment, or leap. Not everyone is at the same point in his or her life or career. Maybe you feel comfortable diving headfirst into a new job or even founding an impact technology company. Or, you might want to stay in your existing job while taking a year or two to try some experiments like working part-time or serving as an advisor to an impact technology company. Or, maybe you're unable to make a change at the moment and are simply hoping to learn more for the future. No matter what stage you're at, I'll suggest practical ways to do so, depending on how much risk you're willing and able to take.

Most of all, I hope you'll stop settling for a horrible job in a world falling apart. Instead, I hope you will join me in being part of something extraordinary—the arrival of a new era of amazing jobs restoring our planet, restoring the American Dream (this time globally) and helping millions of people dramatically improve their lives and prospects—including your own.

CHAPTER 2—THE WAY WE WORK NO LONGER WORKS: THE GREAT RESIGNATION AND THE END OF TOXIC JOBS

Marcus is a pilot who achieved his childhood dream of taking to the skies, but unbeknownst to his wife and two teenage daughters, has taken out a massive personal loan to cover his family's expenses. He isn't sure how other families are managing, but he feels it's impossible to live a normal life without going into debt, and his debts are now way beyond the traditional mortgage and car payments. While the new loan fills him with anxiety, what is really on his mind is his oldest daughter, Annie.

Annie recently developed an interest in climate change, which at first, he thought was great. She had taken an interest in science, and thankfully wasn't into partying like some of her classmates. Yet, the other day, to his horror, she turned on him. In a loud outburst, she accused him of destroying the planet and her future by flying jets emitting huge amounts of greenhouse gases. She then went on social media and posted to hundreds of thousands of followers that the airline industry ferried around rich people, spewing out emissions and destroying the lives of the poor. Not only was Marcus humiliated, but he was angry, and underneath it all, scared. He was nervous some of his colleagues might have seen her post, and more importantly, he couldn't believe how Annie wasn't putting two and two together. They were on the verge of losing everything, and his job, which wasn't easy, was keeping them afloat. How could she be so naïve?

While you may not be a pilot, you might feel similar to Marcus. You did everything right, worked hard, and yet you can't keep up. You're probably concerned about your retirement, and if you have kids, worried about their futures. You're also probably feeling overwhelmed by the many environmental, social, and political issues in the news and aren't sure what to make of it all. What is true and what is false? Is the world falling apart? Is everything coming to an end? Should you be doing something differently?

You're not alone. Around the world, millions of people are feeling the same thing: the American Dream is dead, and the future is bleak. Whether you grew up in the United States or elsewhere, if you believed you could improve your life through hard work and effort, yet nothing seems to be getting any better, this is your new reality. What is going on here? And what can you do about it?

The uncertainty and fear you're feeling today has less to do with your own actions, or the stories of doom and gloom plastering the media every day, and more to do with a massive change our world is undergoing: the Industrial Era has come to an end and the Fourth Industrial Revolution has arrived. You're caught in the transition. You probably remember learning about the Industrial Revolution as a child in your history class. The first Industrial Revolution started in the late 1700s in Britain with the arrival of steel, iron, coal, electricity, the steam engine, textiles, and factories with new machines such as the spinning jenny and power loom. Later, came the telephone, automobiles, radios, airplanes, mass production, and television. In the 1950s we entered the computing age, which really took off in the 1990s bringing computers, the Internet, and globalization to billions of people and companies around the world. Think how different our world is today than it was 300 years ago. Think of the major cities around the world, the transportation networks, the millions of new homes, the energy grids, the schools, and the hospitals. Think of the scientific breakthroughs and technological advances since the late 1700s. Did you know if you were born in the 1800s, there was a 50% chance you'd die before the age of five? If you were lucky enough to survive, you had a 90% chance of living out your life in extreme poverty. It's easy to forget how much life has improved in a few generations and we can thank the Industrial Revolution for that.

But the Industrial Revolution has a dark side. The progress achieved from the Industrial Era came at a huge cost to both our planet and our lives. Companies took as much as they could as fast as they could from the planet and our natural resources, leaving us with a huge mess and countless environmental problems. Companies also created a destructive work culture, working people to the bone in non-stop backbreaking and mind-numbing jobs.

This culture is still with us today, 300 years later. We think of work as tedious, boring, time-consuming, and arduous. We can't wait for the workday to end, to go home, and relax. We can't wait for the weekend. We can't wait until we retire and can start enjoying our lives. At minimum, we must work nine-to-five hour jobs, five days a week, and if that doesn't pay the bills, take on additional hours, working on the weekends or taking on second or third jobs.

In addition to the long work hours, the workplace is also considered a place of stress. We think of bosses and managers as the people in charge of us, who order us around, chastise us, and determine our pay. We feel underappreciated and taken advantage of by co-workers and customers. Worst of all, if we don't work, we can't survive, and thus working takes priority over everything else in life.

Our work culture also emphasizes our job prospects are set in stone when we're teenagers. If we don't go to college, we're destined to string together minimum wage jobs for the rest of our lives. If we choose one career path, it'll be expensive and time consuming to switch. While there are outliers, people who buck the system, dropping out of school to create a successful business, or those who married rich or inherited a fortune and can do whatever they please, most of us are just trying to get by. Yet even those of us who managed to find our dream job, like Marcus the pilot, or those of us in high-paying professional jobs like doctors, lawyers or business executives, often find ourselves drowning in workplace stress and striving to keep up with increasingly expensive lifestyles required by our position and peers.

For a long time, this way of working paid off. Despite the hassle, we could achieve the American Dream, or at least be better off than our parents. Yet over the last few decades, the way we worked, stopped working. While there are multiple explanations for this, in a nutshell, wages no longer kept up with the cost of living, and the stresses and drawbacks of the workplace became intolerable. According to the credit rating company Experian, in the United States, the average person is nearly $100,000 in debt. While we hear about how Millennials can't afford to buy houses and are living with their parents, things are bad for all generations. On average, Baby Boomers are $96,000 in debt, and the Silent Generation, those over 75 years old, are $40,000 in debt. We have created a society where one can work their entire life, and at the end of it, have less money than with which they started.

If that's not enough, there's more. Many people are juggling demanding jobs while caring for young children, spouses, or elderly parents. These care-giving responsibilities can be as demanding as full-time paid jobs, forcing people to drop out of the paid workforce. As the population ages, more people are also retiring or are too ill to work. Those who don't drop out are left to deal with worker shortages or untrained workers who don't know what they're doing. Younger workers, who grew up at the tail end of the Industrial Era and were exposed to the nascent digitization and globalization trends characteristic of the Fourth Industrial Revolution, also have talents and mindsets out of sync with Industrial Era jobs. Industrial Era jobs emphasize hierarchy, staying in your place, and boring routine work, often with the sole goal of making money at the expense of people and the planet. New generations of workers are entrepreneurial, creative, collaborative, and empathetic. They forgo higher salaries to take jobs solving social and environmental challenges. They quickly burn out of jobs going against their talents and generational upbringing.

This burnout, of course, is impacting all generations, and is exacerbated by a world falling apart, damaged by the Industrial Era. In the last few years, the news headlines have been full of disaster after disaster. Forest fires are burning large swaths of North America, Australia, Europe, and South America for weeks at a time scorching entire towns to a crisp. Record-breaking blizzards are burying people alive in their cars. Floods are swallowing up cities and leaving residents without clean water and sewage systems. Hurricanes are pummeling seaside towns, leaving nothing except debris in their wake. Nuclear wars and pandemics are threatening us with existential global disasters, while mass shootings are happening in our schools, shopping malls, and workplaces. Everything feels out of control and the next threat is just around the corner. While hundreds of millions of people are experiencing high levels of stress from simply reading, hearing, or worrying about these problems, others are dealing with these challenges firsthand as their homes burn, their children are shot, or their life savings lost.

When the pandemic struck, everything came to a head. The pandemic, on top of the stress people were already feeling in the workplace and world, was too much to bear. While we know the pandemic was the tipping point for the 2021 Great Resignation when over 47 million Americans voluntarily quit their jobs, quickly followed by "quiet quitting," where up to 50% of the workforce showed up for their paycheck performing as minimal amount of work as possible, burnout, with the workplace and our world, was the culprit. While health concerns, caregiving responsibilities, and financial subsidies may have given workers the push or cushion they needed to make a change, those surveyed said they left because of wage stagnation, rising costs of living, limited opportunities for career advancement, hostile work environments, lack of benefits, inflexible remote work policies, and long-lasting job dissatisfaction.

I believe the Great Resignation is the moment the Industrial Era ended and the Fourth Industrial Revolution began. This has less to do with the arrival of robots or artificial intelligence in the workplace (although that's happening), and everything to do with the moment workers simply walked off the job, whether it was by literally quitting, or for those who couldn't afford to quit, by "quiet quitting." Workers were tired of how they were being treated, how they were being paid, and how their jobs were becoming increasingly meaningless in a world falling apart.

Maybe they also sensed a change in the air. If a worker discovered during the pandemic they could complete their job activities from the comfort of their own couch, managing their own responsibilities and schedule, why would they want to go back to commuting in traffic and having someone order them around all day? If a worker discovered during the pandemic they could double their salary by remotely working for a company across the country, why would they want to go back to the old way of doing things? Everyone saw things could be different. Suddenly there were alternatives to the way we worked, and they were working much better! The old system was cracking. Remarkably, there was no negotiating or arguing during the Great Resignation. There was no desire to stay and try to fix things. There was no bargaining or pleading. The game was over. Everyone simply left their posts and an era ended.

PART II

YOUR DREAM JOB IS HERE

CHAPTER 3—THE IMPACT TECHNOLOGY REVOLUTION: BETTER JOBS, BETTER PAY, BETTER WORLD

After three centuries of living and working in a system saying the only way our society and economy can thrive is by sacrificing ourselves and the planet, an alternative future seems unthinkable—an impossible, idealistic, dream. We have come to believe that if we don't suffer at work, and if we don't tear up our planet by extracting its natural resources, modern life will come to a standstill and our lives will fall apart. What if the opposite is true?

What if Marcus didn't stick it out in his pilot job, going deeper and deeper into debt, fighting more and more with his teenage daughter, and instead took a side job as an advisor to an electric plane startup where he earned additional income and stock by advising the company a few days per month? What if one day, he took his daughter to work with him, and the electric plane startup, learning about Annie's massive social media following, hired her part-time as their social media lead, helping her save money for college while gaining work experience in an exciting new industry she cared about? The technological breakthroughs from the last decade, and the promises of impact technology jobs, makes that happy ending a real possibility for all of us.

I experienced this myself. I had a four-year college degree from one of the world's top universities, yet when I started working, I found myself working multiple weekend and side jobs because my full-time jobs were barely paying me enough to survive. I was often working in hierarchical environments where I was punished for having new ideas, taking initiative, or surrounded by constant bickering and office politics. On my end, I'd plug away, often working until 10 or 11 pm every night as well as weekends. No matter how hard I worked, or how much value I created, rarely did anyone recognize my efforts. I remember one time I only got a small raise after I was so fed up, I refused to leave my boss's office.

Ultimately, I decided to change things. I left the industry and co-founded two impact technology companies in robotics and aerospace, one working on solving a healthcare challenge and another focused on job creation. One did well, and the other was a great learning experience (it didn't work out.) While the term impact technology companies didn't exist at the time, these were two of the world's first. These efforts also positioned me to later find a well-paying job teaching and mentoring others who wanted to create impact technology companies, and ultimately, to write the book you're reading today. The transition took several years and there was a lot of uncertainty. Given I didn't have a lot of savings, I always had to have one full-time job while I explored other opportunities. Ultimately, my efforts and risk-taking paid off, and everything turned out okay.

Looking back, I'm amazed at how much my life changed, and also astounded by how much outdated advice I received over the years about my career and what was possible for me. For example, I was under the assumption that if I wanted to change careers, I would have to make a big change and spend lots of money, such as by going back to school full-time. I was also under the impression that if I didn't have an engineering degree, I could never work with a technology company, let alone found one. Furthermore, I believed if I wanted a job helping other people, I'd have to work for a nonprofit organization and live a life of poverty, sacrifice and suffering. My assumptions were wrong. Within a few years, I went from working at a nonprofit with near poverty-level wages, to co-founding two aerospace and robotics companies and eventually becoming Vice President of a company teaching about impact technology. Furthermore, I was a woman with degrees in History and Southeast Asian studies. None of the career changes I made were supposed to be possible. How did it happen? The secret is, it wasn't just my mindset and actions that changed, although that was part of it. More importantly, the world changed—the possibility for the creation of the first wave of impact technology companies had arrived. I was only smart enough to see the changes coming and take advantage of them.

When and why did these changes happen? After the first and second Industrial Revolutions, along came the Third Industrial Revolution—the arrival of computers on every kitchen table, the Internet, and eventually a smartphone in every pocket. For most of us, that meant we could easily go online to read, listen to music, watch videos, chat with our friends on social media, buy and sell things, as well as carry out daily tasks and errands such as paying bills or booking plane tickets. Some of us even began working remotely for other companies or launching our own online businesses. Companies also began integrating new technologies into their businesses and new technology companies began emerging in new industries.

The Fourth Industrial Revolution builds upon the progress of the Third Industrial Revolution and takes it even further. Under the Fourth Industrial Revolution, we're now putting computers, chips, sensors and software into anything and everything, from our cars to our farm equipment, from our factories to our brains. These computers are extremely advanced, with many using artificial intelligence to carry out tasks, learn, and make decisions by themselves. These computers also talk and interact with one another, sharing information and becoming smarter over time. At the same time, innovations like quantum technologies are promising to speed up computing even more, and as more people around the world start working with technology, and technology becomes more accessible through new interfaces such as Generative AI, more and more companies and innovations are emerging at an ever-faster pace.

It's downright astonishing how quickly computers are transforming everything around us. Computers are running robots in countless factories from car factories to aerospace factories to bakeries. They're working inside laboratories running scientific experiments and mass-producing medicines and vaccines. They're powering robots searching through garbage dumps to find objects to recycle. They're swimming through the ocean studying currents, sea life, and the weather. They're driving autonomous cars and revolutionizing construction by 3D printing houses and other infrastructure. They're inside indoor vertical gardens and roaming through field farms, growing food and weeding plants. Robots are even milking dairy cows.

We also have flying robots such as drones taking pictures and making videos from the skies, and delivering medical goods and lightweight packages. Satellites are a type of robot that can collect data, photos, and even live video feed from space, sending it back to Earth where it can be used from everything to tracking cargo ships to monitoring carbon emissions to documenting villages damaged by natural disasters or war. In all these cases, robots aren't only performing manual labor. They're covered with sensors collecting and analyzing data, checking the quality of products, and helping themselves learn and become more efficient in whatever task they're attempting.

Increasingly, computers are also performing intellectual labor or "desk jobs." Large Language Models (LLMs) are a type of artificial intelligence that read and communicate in text such as words and numbers. Generative AI can also interact with and understand videos, music, artwork, and other non-written mediums, and in turn, can create videos, songs, art, and images at your command. Artificial intelligence is also good at recognizing patterns and can help with tasks such as searching for and identifying tumors on medical images, analyzing the health of a forest from a satellite image, and even deciphering the patterns and potentially meaning, of the songs of whales or birds.

Because computers are able to do all this by turning everything around them into code, and because code can be sent around the world at the speed of light, everything computers do is also highly scalable, meaning innovations and solutions can reach billions of people in the blink of an eye. This allows computers to easily share their data with one another. A robot car driving in San Francisco doesn't need to drive everywhere on the planet to be capable of driving somewhere else. It can download the data already generated by millions of other cars driving all over the world and use that to navigate.

Shockingly, we're now connecting these robots, computers and software to our own bodies and brains. We have prosthetic limbs linked to people's nervous systems. We have sensors that read brainwaves and use artificial intelligence to decipher, in a rudimentary way, what a person is thinking or experiencing. We also have scientists using computers and robots to edit DNA or that can take a few cells, say from say a cow or fish, and use them to grow beef or fish in a bioreactor, all without killing the cow or fish. This field is called cellular agriculture, and it extends to chicken, pork, shrimp, milk, cheese, pet food, and any other protein you can imagine. Scientists are also growing human organs from cells. If you ever need a new heart, lung or kidney, scientists are working on taking your own cells and growing you a new organ so you won't have to wait for someone else to die so you can live. This work is called regenerative medicine, and it intersects with the field of longevity. Now that regenerative medicine is happening, we need to consider we might live much longer than our usual 70-80 years.

It doesn't stop there. Companies are using similar technologies to make lab-grown leather and other materials for clothing, car seats, interior design, and decorating purposes. You can grow these materials in customized and desired shapes, eliminating the need for sewing. You can also grow materials in certain colors without toxic dyes or chemicals, using less water, and generating less pollution. Growing materials and substances from scratch using biology is called biological manufacturing. It's an important component to the future of all manufacturing.

As software, computers and robots become ubiquitous, and as they generate enormous amounts of data and transactions, innovators also created "the blockchain" which permanently and transparently tracks transactions on computers around the world. While many people are using blockchain to engage in speculative cryptocurrency transactions, blockchain has other more practical uses and is helping a lot of businesses be more efficient. Blockchain can track any transaction, from wills and last testaments, to hiring contracts, to a student's grades, to a company's supply chains. Imagine having a perfect and permanent record of a transaction or set of transactions over decades that is incredibly difficult to alter. Imagine also being able to "program" future transactions. For example, you can program a blockchain transaction to pay someone once they have uploaded proof they have completed work. Managers no longer need to do that task.

The World Food Programme, a division of the United Nations with the goal of ending hunger, is using blockchain to send cash assistance to four million people every month in disaster zones or refugee settlements. While previously they primarily shipped food and supplies into disaster areas, today, people can purchase local food or supplies. This system, called "Building Blocks," is quicker, more secure, saves millions of dollars in banking fees, and also supports rather than displaces local farmers and businesses.

Now your first thought in reading all this might be, "Wow, that technology is going to be expensive to build." I would respond with, "Yes, and no." While initially, many advanced technologies are expensive to develop, over time they dramatically fall in cost. This is because of Moore's Law. Back in the 1960s, Gordon Moore, one of the pioneers of the computer chip industry, made an amazing discovery. He noticed computer chips were able to do twice as much work, even as the price to create the chip fell by 50%. He also noticed this didn't happen just once. It happened every 18 months.

Why does this happen? No one knows. It has to do with how the laws of physics work and how information is stored in matter (in this case, on a computer chip.) It's a mind-boggling phenomenon behind the accelerating speed of technological development we're all witnessing today. Think about how expensive the first computers and cell phones were and how cheap they are today and how billions of people now have them. Or consider how it initially cost \$3 billion to sequence the first human genome, yet today costs about \$600. Or think about how anything with a computer in it—whether it's an electric car, a digital camera, or an at-home medical device—has fallen in cost. Or think about all the free things you can access through software and the Internet—online music, books, videos, calculators, maps, spreadsheets, databases, even artificial intelligence. These are free because of Moore's Law and once a digital technology is built, it costs nearly nothing to share it with billions of people (as long as they have a computer and access to an Internet connection.) This is why companies now offer "Freemium" and "Premium" business models and prices. As more and more people around the world have access to these cheap or free technologies, more innovation and ideas are also unleashed, accelerating innovation even more.

Most astonishingly, the pace of change we're witnessing today will seem like a snail's pace in the future. Computing companies today are already using artificial intelligence to speed up computing even more rapidly and profoundly, leaving Moore's Law in the dust, while also lowering costs and energy requirements.

What does computing have to do with social impact, making the world a better place, and impact technology jobs? The ability for technology to scale while also falling in cost is the key driver behind the existence of impact technology companies. Previously, it was too expensive for a company to build the complex solutions needed to solve social problems or get solutions to the billions of people who needed them most at a price they could afford. Computing has fundamentally changed how we solve social problems and the cost of solving social problems. It's an important distinction to wrap your mind around and why we have the first successful impact technology companies today, and why hundreds of thousands more will likely emerge in the future.

Everything I say in this book rests on the idea that new technologies are smart enough, powerful enough, and sophisticated enough to solve our social and environmental problems, and they will be affordable enough for new companies and organizations to form, creating new higher paying jobs in the process. While I personally think working in social impact is morally and ethically the right thing to do, that is not what this book is about. What I am arguing in this book is that new technologies have changed the economics of how we solve social problems. Because of advanced technologies, companies and organizations can now do good in the world, and pay and treat their workers well. Companies can now make money by saving the world rather than exploiting it.

Now your second thought in reading through all of this might be, "How on earth am I going to keep my job with all these new technologies? Aren't all these new technologies going to take away jobs, creating mass unemployment, and making our lives even worse?" Again, I will respond with, "Yes, and no." It's true these technologies will take away jobs, yet they'll also create new and better ones. Importantly, the new jobs will be much better than the old ones. Computers, robots and artificial intelligence will take over the work humans don't want to do—the boring, tedious, low-paying, and dangerous jobs making us watch the clock at the end of the day, crave the weekends, and yearn for retirement.

At the same time, as you will see in the following chapters, new technologies are creating new jobs allowing humans to do more creative, thoughtful, and meaningful work bringing with them higher salaries and dignity. These jobs aren't only more fulfilling, they're jobs doing work previously unimaginable—curing horrific diseases, solving world hunger, ensuring everyone on the planet has clean water and air, allowing us to talk to animals, extend our lives, and more. In this transition, your job is to make sure you're ready for the new opportunities that are part of the impact technology revolution, and find a job you love.

Your final thought in reading this might be, "Even if there are better jobs coming, I'm not convinced these robots and computers are good for humanity. We've already seen the harm done by social media and other technologies. I find these changes scary and don't want any part of this." Good point. I'm scared too. Yet, just as we couldn't stop the previous Industrial Revolutions, we can't stop the Fourth Industrial Revolution. It's already here. We're already in it. Instead, what we must do is ensure we are using technology to help people and work to safeguard against potential problems. Many companies and organizations are hiring teams of technology ethicists for this specific reason. Others are working to make sure technology is designed and inclusive for all types of users. Governments also need policymakers and regulators who know about these topics and can limit their use to specific cases. Others are working in cybersecurity to prevent hackers and criminals from abusing technology. If you care about these issues, the world needs you to step into this work, and it'll be some of our world's most important work.

The possibilities emerging from the Fourth Industrial Revolution will seem magical to us in many ways. Imagine if we can regrow and replace our organs, we might live for hundreds of years! Imagine if we can build houses with 3D printers in a couple of days for a fraction of the cost, we might end homelessness. Imagine if we can grow lab-grown fish, we might end the overfishing of our oceans. Imagine if we can use blockchain to track financial transactions, we might end corruption. Whatever issue you care about, an impact technology company is out there working on it.

CHAPTER 4—ROBOT FARMERS: THE AG TECH AND FOOD TECH WORKFORCE

D o you work in food or agriculture? Whether you're working as a chef in a three-star Michelin restaurant, a truck driver hauling the nation's food supply across the country, managing a cattle ranch like Luis, planting or harvesting crops, or perpetually waitressing the night shift, you're part of the largest workforce on the planet. Over 3 billion people work in jobs devoted to growing, transporting, preparing, and selling food. It's one of our world's most important industries and one also undergoing rapid technological change. According to Tracxn, a company tracking innovation, there are over 23,000 companies working in Ag Tech and 25,000 working in Food Tech with more emerging every day. From seed to plate, these companies are transforming our food and agricultural industries on a global scale.

If you work in food and agriculture, you might not initially think of yourself as someone who solves social and environmental challenges, but your work is closely linked to both. During the Industrial Era, the food and agricultural industries were responsible for feeding the planet and helping humanity thrive, but at great cost to the environment and society. Did you know nearly half of our planet's forests, shrubs, and grasslands have been destroyed to create land for farming and livestock? Forests absorb and store carbon and without them, too much carbon goes into the atmosphere, warming the planet. Growing and transporting food also creates greenhouse gases, while fertilizer and pesticides create pollution and run-off. As greenhouse gases lead to climate change, and land is over-farmed, a feedback loop happens. Farmers face more droughts, floods, and natural disasters, and respond by overfarming more, worsening the cycle. Those who can't work harder go into debt, and often out of business, or worse. In India, nearly 10,000 farmers commit suicide every year because of debt. In some low-income countries, where 80% of the population works in food or agriculture, large scale economic problems can unfold impacting the well-being of entire nations for decades.

In addition to environmental and social issues, food plays an important role in our health. An overabundance of unhealthy food created by the Industrial Era has led to hundreds of millions of people suffering from diabetes, obesity and other diseases, while globally, over 800 million people go hungry each day. Our food system is out of balance and needs help.

The Industrial Era also led to food and agricultural workers facing some of the most challenging working conditions. Agricultural workers perform backbreaking labor in severe heat. Truck drivers spend countless hours on the road giving up time with their friends and family. Food service workers labor late into the night for low wages and tips, dealing with disgruntled and unhappy customers, or working over hot greasy stoves for hours on end. Having grown up in the Industrial Era, and having worked in food service as a teenager, I just accepted such work as part of life. It wasn't fun, but it was work. But what if things could be different? What if technology could help?

A few years ago, I met with members of a farmworker community in the United States. I wanted to understand how they felt about the possibility of robots and farming equipment taking their jobs. While I assumed they would fight tooth and nail against these machines, I was wrong. They told me their jobs were awful and robots should take them. They explained they spent long hours working outside in hot weather that often reached 114 degrees Fahrenheit or higher. They permanently injured their backs with repetitive labor or faced injuries from equipment. They were exposed to pesticides, diseases, insects, snakes, pollution, and smoke from wildfires. While some farms treated their workers well, others constantly violated labor laws forcing employees to work in dangerous conditions such as extremely hot weather without access to shade, water, or bathroom breaks. Farming is also linked to human trafficking and poor living conditions.

The farmers I spoke with told me no human should be doing the work they're doing, and robots should be doing this work. However they also told me they didn't want to just leave their jobs and industry, but they wanted to help build the robots and pioneer the future Ag Tech industry. They pointed out they had decades of valuable experience in farming and agriculture that could be helpful in ensuring new farming technologies worked properly and were useful.

As I learned more about the automation of the agricultural industry, I was happy to learn there are farmers at the forefront of creating new Ag Tech startups. I also learned that some older farmers are now working with their children or grandchildren to digitize and modernize their farms. In the past, the children of farmers would often grow up and head to the city for better jobs. Today, the children and grandchildren of farmers are learning about technology in school and then coming home to work with their elders or start their own Ag Tech startups. While we often hear about how technology displaces workers, the flip side is workers already in an industry have a huge competitive advantage in pioneering the next generation of their industry because of their insider knowledge. They can be part of making their industry safer, healthier, and greener, as well as more efficient and profitable.

How are the new Ag Tech and Food Tech impact technology companies helping solve social and environmental challenges? Some of the most interesting work is happening in vertical and robotic farms, cellular agriculture, autonomous restaurants and robotic chefs, and addressing food waste. Let's take a deep dive into these sectors and companies.

Vertical and Robotic Farms

Have you recently strolled through the grocery store and noticed the herb and lettuce section is now populated with a number of brightly packaged new items? Chances are, these are vegetables that were grown in a vertical or robotic farm. Vertical and robotic farming is one of the fastest growing sectors in Ag Tech. Vertical farms are farms set up inside warehouses, often on shelves stacked sky high, in indoor climate-controlled spaces. Robotic farms can be integrated into vertical farms or can take the shape of portable gardening containers situated on the ground that can be moved, managed and tended by robots. Some well-known vertical and robotic farming companies include Bowery Farming, Plenty, Aerofarms, Freight Farms, and Gotham Greens. Amazon is backing a vertical farm company called Hippo Harvest. According to the research company Research and Markets, the vertical farming industry was valued at $5.1 billion in 2023 and expected to grow to $15.3 billion by 2028.

Why would farmers want to grow their crops indoors with robots rather than in traditional farm fields? Healthy arable outdoor land is getting harder and harder to find because of soil depletion, land shortages, drought, and changing weather patterns. It's also expensive to transport food into cities where customers live, creates greenhouse gases, and food can spoil along the way. Robotic farms also save farmers a lot of money in fertilizer, water, and other inputs as they use over 90% less water and fertilizer than a traditional farm. A robotic farm has sensors that can detect when a plant needs water or fertilizer, and the system can simply apply a few drops. A traditional farm requires one to indiscriminately douse large swaths of land with water and fertilizer, much of it evaporating or turning into run-off.

Indoor farms can also help people living in food deserts. Imagine if you live in a neighborhood populated only with convenience stores and fast-food restaurants. A nearby indoor robotic farm can supply you with fresh vegetables, even during a cold, snowy, winter. These farms are also sealed off from damaging weather, storms, wind, as well as hungry wildlife and pests, allowing them to skip the pesticides and other deterrents.

While these benefits might sound great, the advantages run even deeper. Farms infused with technology are connected and data-driven. They're constantly collecting data about the health and development of the plants and nutrient levels. If a certain herb is particularly tasty, a farmer can go back and look at the data for that exact plant and re-create the exact conditions to grow more. Now imagine what this data means for the whole food system, because it's not only farms that are connected, but everything else is also connected. Imagine you place an order to buy parsley during your next online grocery delivery order. Theoretically, a message could be instantly sent to a robot planting parsley seeds on a farm, as well as alerting trucks and stores that will later be involved in transporting and selling the plant. This connectivity, when it happens at scale, can make our entire food and logistic systems more predictable, efficient, and affordable.

While vertical and robotic farms are off to a good start, field farmers don't want to be left behind and are adding technology into their operations at a fantastic pace. They argue vertical farms might be useful in urban areas or smaller countries but can't compete with a traditional field farm and their massive amounts of land. They also claim unless an indoor farm has access to clean energy, the energy used by the light bulbs in indoor farms is still creating too many greenhouse gases.

Traditional field farms are now using robots that can prepare soil, plant seeds, pull out or zap weeds, tend plants, and harvest crops. Big companies, including John Deere and Caterpillar are building these technologies, as well as startups like Dahlia Robotics, Naïo Technologies, Agrobot, Bear Flag Robotics (acquired by John Deere), Blue River Technologies (acquired by John Deere), and ecoRobotix. These companies are building autonomous farming equipment using computer vision and artificial intelligence to navigate, as well as harvest crops and remove weeds. Some of these robots can be programmed to communicate and collaborate with one another and some are electric, using batteries producing fewer emissions and pollution. Some startups believe by supplying smaller field farms with robotic equipment, these smaller farms will be able to compete with the bigger farms instead of being driven out of business.

Alphabet (Google) has a division of their company supporting "Moonshots" and recently spun out an Ag Tech startup called Mineral. Mineral has built a low-emissions robotic rover that can drive through fields and collect images and data about plants. Mineral combines this data with data from satellites and other sources to understand the best growing conditions for different types of plants. As of 2023, they had mapped 10% of the world's farmland. While this knowledge can help individual farms, they have a bigger mission of using their data to try to feed everyone on the planet in a sustainable way. Mineral is a great example of how robotic farm equipment does more than save a farmer manual labor. Once you start digitizing the farming ecosystem, you can do a lot with that data.

Robotic farming equipment is also revolutionizing farming in lower income countries. Hello Tractor is one of Africa's early Ag Tech companies launched in 2015 and invested in by John Deere. Hello Tractor allows people to share tractors and track Ag Tech data meeting a huge need in a region where it's difficult for farmers to purchase expensive equipment on their own.

ThriveAgric, based in Nigeria, is working with 800,000 farmers using data to link them to financing and local markets. They have already created over 9000 jobs and are hoping their solution will increase the wages of over 15 million farmers, all while improving access to food and reducing loss of food to spoilage.

ThriveAgric also illustrates how, counter-intuitively, technology doesn't always lead to technological unemployment. In regions where ThriveAgric works, the legacy agricultural system is so inefficient that markets are broken. Better technologies are fixing the markets, allowing more people to buy food. As more people buy food, more higher-paying jobs are created. As of 2023, there were over 230 new Ag Tech startups in Africa, and what is happening in Africa is also happening in Asia, South Asia, and Latin America. As the Ag Tech industry expands around the world, it can repair more broken markets, creating more jobs, bringing more healthy food to the people who need it most.

Cellular Agriculture

Would you eat beef, chicken or shrimp grown in a lab? What about milk or cheese? What about a cookie made with lab-grown eggs? Cellular agriculture refers to growing proteins either directly from cells themselves or genetically engineering yeast or bacteria to produce the foods. Today, scientists are able to take a sample of cells from a living creature without killing it, like a cow, chicken, pig, or fish, put them in a bioreactor and grow and replicate those cells creating lab-grown steaks, filets, pork, and more. No one needs to spend years raising, feeding and caring for livestock, let alone slaughtering them. In addition, there's no need to destroy forests or sensitive ecosystems to make room for livestock or overfish the oceans and seas.

Scientists are also able to genetically engineer yeast or bacteria to produce milk, honey, vanilla, coffee, oils, lab-grown leather, and other substances. The company C16 Biosciences has figured out how to use biotechnology and fermentation to create lab-grown palm oil. Palm oil is used in countless daily products but harms the environment. When farmers raze rainforests to make room for palm oil plantations, they're destroying natural carbon sinks and the homes of wildlife, endangered species, and indigenous populations. Lab-grown palm oil causes none of that.

If you're like most people, you might react to the thought of eating lab-grown steak with disgust. But, like many people, you might change your mind once you learn some of its advantages. Lab-grown steaks are biologically similar to steaks grown in a cow. Wouldn't you rather eat a lab-grown steak than a steak involving the confinement and killing of a sentient animal? Beef is one of the foods most significantly contributing to climate change, both through the emission of greenhouse gases, as well as through deforestation resulting from clearing land for cattle to graze. Raising livestock is also inefficient. It takes years to raise, feed, and care for livestock, and only a few weeks to grow lab-grown food. Lab-grown food might someday improve your health. Theoretically, scientists can customize lab-grown food by adding vitamins, reducing fat, or personalizing it to a person's specific dietary needs. You can also grow lab-grown food anywhere. It can help end hunger by getting quality protein to anyone, anywhere.

Whether you decide to eat this food or not, the industry is growing. According to Straits Research, as of 2021, the cellular agriculture industry was valued at $134 billion and expected to grow to $515 billion by 2030. There are several hundred cellular agricultural companies working in lab-grown meat, proteins, seafood, and bio fabrics. There are also companies using biological manufacturing to create pet food, and companies working on perfumes, make-up, and other substances. While some may frown on the genetic engineering involved in biological manufacturing, others see it as a way to eliminate the toxic chemicals in our current products. It's a double-edged sword.

Some of the leading companies growing lab-grown beef, chicken and pork include Mosa Meat, Aleph Farms, Believer Meats, Upside Farms, Eat Just, Good Meat, Uncommon, and Meatable. BlueNalu, FinlessFoods and WildType are creating lab-grown seafood. There are now countless companies, similar to C16 Biosciences, using organisms to produce foods, medicines and fabrics. Gingko Bioworks has fleets of robots genetically engineering organisms to create everything from skincare products to therapeutics. Imagine being able to take the DNA from a rose, inserting it into an organism, and having that organism produce the scent of a rose and flavor on demand. Those scents and flavors can be used in perfumes, lotions, make-up and desserts.

In addition to the many companies creating products through cellular agriculture, other companies are working in adjacent industries such as in building bioreactors, or producing the nutrients, mediums and scaffolds needed for the cells to grow in bioreactors. Biological manufacturing is an expanding field with many subsectors, all creating new companies and jobs.

Autonomous Restaurants and Robotic Chefs

Have you noticed how technology has been creeping into restaurants and grocery stores over the last few years? First it was scanners and self-checkout lines in grocery stores, then apps for ordering take-out food, then kiosks popping up inside McDonald's, then McDonald's and Chipotle announcing they're experimenting with robots to cook french fries and tortilla chips and make guacamole. Next, it's Generative AIs taking your drive-thru orders.

If you live in a big city, you might have even dined at a robotic salad or grain bowl shop. Behind the scenes, companies are also building autonomous food delivery trucks and all sorts of new inventory and logistical systems. One of the most intriguing startups I have come across is CloudChef.

CloudChef uses artificial intelligence to allow anyone to have a world-class chef-cooked meal. The twist is the chef is you, or someone else who has never set foot in a kitchen. CloudChef works by setting up studios, similar to recording studios, where cameras, thermal sensors, and other technologies record the chefs as they prepare meals. They use sensors and artificial intelligence to capture every detail of how that meal is made, including recording information such as the way a chef stirs a pot, or a certain texture or color a food becomes when cooked, that wouldn't normally be noted and conveyed in a traditional cookbook.

Their system translates this information into such precise instructions that a person with no formal training can cook a meal just as good as one cooked by one of our world's top chefs. The founders of CloudChef, who are based in the United States, but hail from India, were inspired to create the company because they had trouble finding authentic tasting Indian food in the United

States.

Several world-famous chefs have invested in CloudChef. While initially you might assume a human chef would worry about an artificial intelligence chef stealing his or her recipes and knowledge, the opposite is happening. A chef who works with CloudChef receives a royalty for every meal created, whether in a restaurant or someone's home. In this sense, the future isn't about artificial intelligence taking human jobs, it's about artificial intelligence and humans collaborating to make things better and reach more people. Why should only a few people have access to meals prepared by the world's best chefs when millions or billions of people can? And why would a chef only want to feed a handful of people over his or her lifetime, when he or she could instead feed millions or billions of people and earn royalties on each of those meals? CloudChef challenges us to think about using technology to literally expand the pie for all.

Solving for Food Waste

Did you know that about 35% of the food supply is wasted in the United States? We aren't talking about the leftovers in your refrigerator here, although that's part of it. Food is wasted at the farm, in factories, during transportation, and grocery stores throw out spoiled food before it even reaches you. This statistic is true in most countries around the world, and even higher in countries with poor food storage infrastructure. Luckily, there are a number of new companies building technologies to address this problem.

The Crover Robot burrows through large silos of grain. It uses sensors to check the moisture and temperature of the grain and sends a message to a farmer's smartphone if it finds a problem. Pests can infest grain stored at the wrong temperature and it can also spoil or develop dangerous fungus. A little burrowing robot can climb deep inside the grain silo checking up on things 24 hours per day. In fact, up to 10% of grain is spoiled every year— enough to feed 250 million people.

A participant I met at Singularity University, Abi Ramanan, is the founder of a company called ImpactVision. ImpactVision was a hyperspectral imaging company (spectroscopy combined with computer vision to measure reflectance across hundreds of wavelengths of light) and machine learning to provide real-time, non-invasive food quality information about parameters like freshness or ripeness or the presence of contaminants to enable agrifood companies to make better data-driven decisions about how they ripen, process, sort and distribute food to reduce waste, improve yields, deliver more consistent quality for consumers and prevent product recalls. The mission of the company was to tackle the $1 trillion global food waste problem, which currently contributes 8% of global greenhouse gas emissions. In February 2020, ImpactVision was acquired by Apeel Sciences, a company developing a plant-based solution to extend produce shelf-life and preserve quality.

Other companies working to reduce food waste include Full Harvest, Hungry Harvest, Imperfect Foods, and Nilus. They work to sell "ugly produce" or food that doesn't look perfect but hasn't spoiled, at lower prices points, or improve the distribution and accessibility of foods. Neurolabs and Tenzo help stores and restaurants better predict their food demand, allowing them to only purchase the food they'll need.

Atlas Organics is a composting company in San Antonio, Texas, working with AMP Robotics and the City of San Antonio, to use robots to remove contaminants from compost. Their system, which uses artificial intelligence trained with previous images of contaminants, can recognize contaminants on a conveyor belt, and uses a robot with suction cup arms to remove the contaminants. Atlas Organics was recently acquired by Generate Capital, which has provided them with $200 million in funding for expansion.

What do you think of these companies and organizations? Would you enjoy working beside robots on a vertical farm or creating slaughter-free meat? Do you want to reduce food waste? Are you passionate about helping people access healthier food?

Do you want to keep emission from food out of the environment? These are just a few of the companies you might want to consider.

Identifying Impact Technology Companies

We opened this chapter noting there are nearly 50,000 new companies working in Ag Tech and Food Tech. How do you know if these companies are impact technology companies? How do you distinguish impact technology companies from other types of companies? While impact technology companies will be using technology, being an impact technology company requires more than that. After all, a food company could be using advanced technologies to create junk food, emitting excessive greenhouse gas emissions, and putting their worker's lives in danger with unsafe equipment.

Two of the primary ways I've developed for identifying impact technology companies is that they are mission-oriented (they are solving an important social or environmental problem), and they treat their workers and customers with dignity. While our next section will explore what these criteria look like in Ag Tech and Food Tech companies, you can use the same criteria to identify impact technology companies in other industries such as Ed Tech, Health Tech, Climate Tech, or other industries you come across in this book or your life.

Impact Technology Companies are Mission-Oriented

One of the hallmarks of impact technology companies is that they're mission-oriented. While many traditional companies will only talk about how wonderful their product is and why you should buy it, impact technology companies talk about their mission, the social and environmental problems they are trying to solve, and their solutions to those problems. For example, the website of a major vertical farming company states they can grow 350 times more food than a traditional farm, with a fraction of the environmental footprint. They also share with their customers the problems associated with traditional agriculture, including how we have lost 40% of the Earth's land to farming and cattle, use 70% of our water on food, and how the food and agriculture industry (including transportation) contributes to 40% of greenhouse gas emissions. They then share how they are addressing these specific problems. They use 1% of the land of a traditional farm, dramatically less inputs, and have farms in both rural and urban areas reducing transport costs and emissions.

Another major vertical farming company notes on their website that by 2050 we'll need to feed 9 billion people, with even less arable land than we have today. They share how this problem is related to population growth, water scarcity, arable land loss, overuse of pesticides, and supply chain challenges. They share how they use 99% less land than field farms, 95% less water, and zero pesticides.

Agrosmart, a Brazilian company founded by Mariana Vasconcelos, a participant I met at Singularity University, is now the largest Ag Tech data company in Latin America. If you go to the Agrosmart website, the company's headline is not about agriculture or technology, but about how they are solving climate change by transforming our food systems. Everything about the company feels mission-oriented.

In contrast, if you go to the websites of other companies, they don't share their missions and the problems they're trying to solve, but just focus on advertising their product in traditional ways, such as by featuring celebrities or actors and actresses happily consuming their product. Sometimes companies will also "greenwash." This means they are selling a product that is unhealthy and bad for society and the planet, but they will make a donation to a social or environmental cause, or run a small, superficial project that is good for people and the planet. They want to give the impression they are doing good, when in reality they are making things worse.

I view impact technology companies as distinct from companies practicing corporate social responsibility (CSR) or Environmental, Social and Governance (ESG) best practices.

Both CSR and ESG are practices developed to keep Industrial Era companies in check. In the Industrial Era, there was an assumption that a company would sacrifice profits, if it also engaged in behaviors that supported workers, society, or the environment. At a high level, both CSR and ESG were developed to give companies the ability to do good in the world, even if it hurt profits. While impact technology companies may resemble companies practicing CSR and ESG in some ways, they are different because they are not part of the Industrial Era, and do not face the same challenge in balancing profit and purpose. Because impact technology companies are exploiting technology, rather than people and the environment, they don't need CSR and ESG to keep them in check. Impact technology companies are making money by solving society's social and environmental challenges so purpose and profit are the same thing.

Impact Technology Companies Treat their Workers and Customers with Dignity

Another hallmark of impact technology companies is they treat their workers and customers with dignity. While impact technology companies are solving major social and environmental problems, they're also profitable or on the way to being profitable. Impact technology companies won't ask you to work for extremely low wages or as a volunteer simply because the work is doing good in the world. Similarly, they will do their best to make their products and services affordable to everyone. At a high level, this means the investors and owners of impact technology companies are willing to share their profits with their workers through wages and stock, as well as through lower prices with their customers. Some also create business models where their customers can also have ownership in the company.

In researching impact technology companies, you can find this information under the salaries and benefits section in their job descriptions. Most impact technology companies in the United States will pay full-time professional staff starting salaries of $100,000. They'll offer unskilled labor or part-time labor compensation between $20-$40 per hour. For example, one vertical farming company's recruiting site advertises that a public relations manager will earn between $124,00 and $136,00 per year, and a maintenance technician will receive $40 per hour. Impact technology companies may also offer stock options. Because technology companies can scale quickly, they'll grow slowly the first few years, and later scale, sometimes to millions or billions of customers. When that happens, the company becomes financially valuable, and those who hold stock can find themselves with enough money to purchase a home, pay college tuition, or even retire. While this doesn't happen with every company, it's more common with technology companies. Impact technology companies also often offer both professional and unskilled labor benefits including dental, vision, health insurance, disability, paid holidays, paternity and maternity leave, as well as 401K contributions.

In thinking about compensation and benefits, it's important to keep your context in mind. Salaries will be very different for impact technology companies in the United States versus Bangladesh or Brazil. Salaries in certain impact technology industries, such as electric autonomous cars will be higher than impact technology companies working in rural community healthcare or social justice. Young startups may not be able to afford high salaries but will offer equity and the chance to play a leading role in the company. Given the wide variety of impact technology companies and compensation, the important thing to consider is that in the Industrial Era, you had to choose between doing good and a decent salary. Today, that's no longer true. Today, if you want to take a low-paying job in exchange for purpose, you can, but you can also find a higher-paying job and have a life-long career in social impact if you want. You now have a choice.

Throughout this book, my goal is to give you a wide variety of examples of impact technology companies across the spectrum. I will include examples of impact technology companies that pay their employees extremely well, many that will pay you a decent and dignified salary, and even a few nonprofits and government programs that are doing outstanding work at the intersection of technology and social impact. Later in the book, we will also discuss where you are in your life professionally and financially, and how you can use this information to find the right job for you.

In addition to compensating their employees fairly, impact technology companies also value the well-being of their employees. They want employees who are happy, capable and can grow with the company. Many impact technology companies offer on the job training programs, wellness programs, educational courses, fellowships, career coaches, financial coaches, and community service or family days. Some impact technology companies also carry out their social impact mission through hiring. They will state on their websites they hire from local communities, hire those with only high school degrees, and hire people who were incarcerated.

Impact technology companies also don't adhere to the hierarchies of the Industrial Era and instead focus on unleashing human potential as quickly as possible and promoting teamwork and collaboration. Many state they hire for teamwork and collaboration over individual success and emphasize teamwork and collegiality in their job descriptions. You can also look at the biographies of existing employees to see if talented people rise to the top, or if the company prioritizes the Industrial Era way of "doing one's time" and holding people back.

When you're evaluating impact technology companies, use your common sense. We are at the very beginning of the impact technology revolution. You will find some companies are outstanding examples of impact technology companies, meeting all the criteria, while others may have good intentions but are struggling. Some impact technology companies may be mission-oriented, but facing unexpected financial troubles. Some may be doing well in terms of their mission and finance, but have hired managers that don't understand how to mentor and create opportunities for new employees. As you evaluate companies, think about what aspects of impact technology companies are most important to you, and if you come across challenges, try to understand if they are temporary problems that can be fixed or something more significant.

Now that we have discussed how to identify impact technology companies, let's explore some of the jobs these companies are offering. While we will do a deep dive into food and agriculture jobs in this section, what you learn here is transferable to the impact technology job of your choice.

What Types of Jobs are Available at Impact Technology Companies?

While impact technology companies are known for using technology, and appreciate workers interested in technology, they hire people with both technical and non-technical skills. For example, many vertical and robotic farming companies are hiring engineers and experts in robotics and computer-vision. They are also hiring for roles in production, sales, business development, marketing, business operations, technology, and human resources.

Jobs in production include overseeing the construction of facilities for new farms, making sure new farms are in compliance with laws and regulations, and scouting out new farm sites. Jobs in sales, business development, and marketing involve helping customers understand vertical farming, representing the brand, and cultivating new customers and partnerships. Business Operations includes finance, accounting, supporting the CEO's office, legal, program management, supply chains and logistics. Jobs in human resources include recruiting and hiring new employees, helping retain existing employees, and general operations. Within these categories, there are also jobs available at all levels. These companies need Vice Presidents, and they need janitors.

As you can see, many of these futuristic companies still need workers who have the everyday skills necessary for making a company or organization successful. One of the reasons I wanted to write this book is to help workers understand this—you may be working in a job today that you hate and that is destroying our planet and making people miserable, when you have the skills to take a job with a company that will treat you much better, and make our world a better place!

Are These Jobs Really Helping?

Now, what if you have read thus far and are feeling scared out of your mind by these companies and can only think about everything that might go wrong? What will happen if new companies can't create new jobs fast enough to prevent technological unemployment? What will happen if vegetables raised in vertical farms aren't as healthy as those raised in traditional soil? What will happen if lab-grown meat is unhealthy? What if building and running all these new companies turns out to be more carbon intensive than our existing solutions, or they damage the environment in other ways we haven't considered? These are all legitimate and important questions, and we need to consider them not just for the food and agriculture industries, but all the new impact technology industries.

If you're concerned about these issues, you can now find a job specifically dealing with these sorts of questions. If you're concerned about job loss, you can work with an Ed Tech company helping reskill and retrain adult workers, or become a career coach. You could also propose to a local university or your city government that they establish a startup incubator in your hometown to help your community create new companies and jobs. If you're concerned about the future of farming, you could work with a regenerative agriculture company. Regenerative farms focus on restoring the soil, protecting water resources and biodiversity, and supporting local farmers and communities. Some are also impact technology companies using technology to monitor their efforts. Think tanks and universities are hiring people to analyze the costs, benefits, and risks of cellular agriculture.

As we go deeper into the future, our job is to have the wisdom to take the benefits of new technologies that can save lives and heal the planet, but also use them wisely and preserve certain valuable ways of life from the past. As we explore more industries, this theme will come up again and again.

It's also an important reason, why, regardless of how you feel about these companies, that you get involved in learning about or working with impact technology companies. We need your experience and perspective to ensure the future works for everyone. We need those of you who are most wary of these new technologies to actually help build them, because you will think about everything that can go wrong and design ways to protect against those problems. Remember, you're one of the first workers of the impact technology revolution. What you do today will help determine how this new era unfolds, possibly, for billions of people.

CHAPTER 5—SAVING THE PLANET: THE CLIMATE AND GREEN TECH WORKFORCE

T wenty-two miles off the coast of Southern California sits a small island many consider paradise. With wild bison, dolphins, manta rays and blue skies as far as the eye can see, Catalina Island beckons from another era. The island's only town, Avalon, has no cars and resembles 1920s America. Despite this breathtaking beauty, there's one problem. A few years ago, a robot swimming in the waters between Catalina Island and Los Angeles discovered something startling. Someone had dumped toxic waste across the ocean floor. Prior to the Marine Protection Research and Sanctuaries Act of 1972, it was common for companies and governments to dump waste into the ocean to dispose of it. There are now a suspected 25,000 barrels of DDT, a pesticide banned by most of the world, on the seafloor off the coast of Los Angeles and Catalina, as well as ammunition, depth charges, and military smoke devices dumped after World War II. Scientists sent a robot out to investigate after detecting DDT in dolphins in Southern California as well as discovering an extremely aggressive cancer in nearby sea lions. Unfortunately, the dumping site off Los Angeles isn't an anomaly. Coastlines around the world are littered with similar debris, much of it dumped decades ago and long forgotten.

If you leave Catalina Island and sail thousands of miles northwest further into the Pacific Ocean, you'll find another remnant of the Industrial Era, the Great Pacific Garbage Patch. This area, about twice the size of Texas, is full of plastics and trash ranging from flip-flips to fishing nets to floating laundry baskets. Garbage from rivers in Asia and the Americas pools into this specific spot because of how the ocean currents flow. While some of the debris is visible and recognizable, much of it is breaking down into micro plastics, harder to see and retrieve. This isn't a corporate dumping site from decades past, but trash left by all of us every day—the consumers dependent on plastics as a way of life. While much of the trash was improperly disposed of, even those of us who put our waste in garbage dumps have contributed to this debris as storms and floods can carry waste from overflowing dumps out into the ocean.

Our Industrial Era has polluted our land and air as well as our oceans and waterways. Communities and sensitive ecosystems around the world are exposed to toxins and runoff from landfills, mines, and farms. Air pollution is a problem in almost every location around the globe, contributing to lung cancer, asthma, dementia, stroke, diabetes and other diseases. Carbon dioxide, methane, and other greenhouse gases are triggering climate change, and creating severe weather, flooding, wildfires and droughts. Today we're witnessing catastrophic climate-related events killing thousands of people at a time and creating billions of dollars in damage.

My guess is you probably feel extremely frustrated by these challenges and also somewhat lost. You might believe governments should be passing stricter laws or companies should be taking more responsibility for the damage they're causing. Perhaps you're joining protests advocating for change or trying to lower your carbon footprint by changing your lifestyle only to find today's society and economy offers you few options to do so in a practical way. Up until a few years ago, individual efforts and activism were our only choices for dealing with these problems. Today, this is no longer the case. There are now tens of thousands of impact technology startups and companies leading efforts to solve our climate and environmental problems—once and for all. These companies aren't greenwashing or practicing business as usual while they contribute to environmental causes on the side. They're building new companies and business models around solutions directly solving climate and environmental challenges.

Impact technology companies are solving climate and environmental challenges in three ways. The first group is mapping, analyzing and increasing our understanding of climate change and environmental destruction. The second group is manually cleaning up the messes and damage created by the Industrial Era. The third group is creating new companies, or transforming existing companies, to build Industrial Era products in ways less damaging to our planet and society.

Increasing Our Understanding of the Challenges

Given the size of our planet, that pollution and emissions are often invisible, and damage can take decades to occur, it's difficult to track climate and environmental challenges. If we can't see the problem, it's hard to solve it.

If you enjoy researching problems or communicating complex problems in easy-to-understand ways, mapping and monitoring climate and environmental challenges might be for you. While this type of work involves collecting data and preparing reports, it also involves creativity—using graphic design skills to visually present problems, or creating videos, movies, or story-telling projects to help people better understand the problems.

A number of new startups and companies are using technology to monitor and track problems from land, sea and sky. Satellite companies Planet, Spire, and Constellr are using cameras and sensors in outer space to monitor our planet's health from above. Planet has a constellation of about 200 small satellites monitoring the Earth on a daily basis and uses historical satellite data to track environmental changes. One of their key products is Forest Carbon, which allows companies, governments, nonprofits and journalists to track the world's trees from above. They can measure how forest fires, logging, or clear cutting are damaging forests anywhere.

You can also use their technology to monitor reforestation efforts. This is important as many companies are purchasing carbon-offset credits. When companies pollute, if they purchase offset credits, other companies or organizations will be paid to replant forests or engage in other work to offset the damage they did. Satellite data can verify completed work. The satellite company Spire, uses satellite and other data to measure the Earth's environment and atmosphere, including ocean wind speed, soil moisture, flooding, and sea ice. Constellr collects thermal data from the Earth to measure water temperatures and heat. Other satellite companies are tracking the leaking of methane gas in real time, the melting of polar ice caps, illegal fishing and logging, the impact of droughts and natural disasters, and data helping farmers grow food in planet-friendly ways.

It isn't just satellite companies collecting data about the Earth. A few years ago I met an employee from a company called Saildrone. Saildrone builds autonomous surfboard-like vessels powered by solar energy and sails. These vessels go far out into the ocean, surviving the harshest conditions, collecting data about the seawater to help manage climate change and map the oceans. Other companies and research institutions are building underwater vessels collecting environmental DNA, or e-DNA. Plant and sea life shed DNA into the water around them and we can use it to better understand biodiversity, ecosystems, and endangered species.

A few years ago, Google and the National Ocean and Atmospheric Administration's Pacific Island Fisheries Science Center, began using artificial intelligence to better understand the songs of humpback whales, looking for insights on behavior and migration patterns. While this knowledge might be helpful in protecting whales from ships or other threats, a group called the Earth Species Project is going even further, using artificial intelligence to decode non-human communication, with the ultimate goal of interspecies communication. Can you imagine being able to talk to whales, dolphins, and the millions of other species with whom we share the planet? Can you imagine that being your job?

While some startups and companies collect data, other

companies use this data to change behaviors that are harming the planet. Unilever, one of the world's largest household goods companies, works with Orbital Insight to use satellite and other data to ensure their products aren't using palm or soybean oil connected to deforestation.

As we discussed earlier, the computing company NVIDIA is working on a massive data project called Earth-2. Earth-2 is a digital twin of our planet modeling climate, weather, natural resources and more. Their technology allows climate scientists to view and simulate how weather will behave down to the kilometer and can help with predicting natural disasters and managing agricultural, transportation and other industries. Earth-2 will also help people run accurate simulations predicting how their actions, such as limiting or increasing greenhouse gases, will impact the planet, businesses, and communities.

Together, these companies and others are helping us understand how big and complex our climate and environmental problems are, as well as pinpointing the most efficient and powerful ways to address them. This work also sets the stage for other companies, governments, and organizations, to help repair our planet, reversing and cleaning up damage from decades past.

The Great Clean Up

When I was a child, every day I would see an old man in his late 80s, walking through my hometown picking up trash. I lived in a town of a few thousand people with only one main street. Despite such a close-knit population, every day there was enough garbage for this old man to spend hours picking it up. It turns out this old man was Paul Squibb, a descendent from the founders of the Bristol Myers Squibb pharmaceutical company. Despite his famous connection, it was never below him to go out and do the dirty work, even in his old age, to keep our town clean and beautiful.

Today, given the amount of trash and pollution in our world, in addition to heroes like Paul Squibb, we also need technology to help clean up the planet. Many companies and organizations are building robots and other technical solutions to do exactly that

Earlier we learned about the Great Pacific Garbage Patch where trash is accumulating in the Pacific Ocean in staggering amounts. What I didn't tell you is that an organization, called The Ocean Clean Up, founded by Boyan Slat at the age of 18 in the Netherlands, is already out there cleaning up the garbage. The Ocean Clean Up estimates the Great Pacific Garbage Patch is home to 1.8 trillion pieces of plastic. They're cleaning up the trash through two different approaches. Out in the Pacific Ocean they have ships and a barrier net collecting the plastic, which they haul out of the ocean, put on ships, and recycle or take to proper dumps. They use computational modeling to determine where plastics will concentrate based on water currents, helping them get the best hauls. So far, they've cleaned up 22 million pounds of trash and are working on an even more efficient collection system.

They're also stopping the problem at its source by placing robotic boats and capture systems at the mouths of rivers. These systems capture trash before it enters the ocean. There are currently systems in rivers in Indonesia, Malaysia, Vietnam, the Dominican Republic, Guatemala, the United States, Jamaica, and Thailand. In the future, they aim to place capture systems in over 1000 rivers around the world.

Other technology companies are also cleaning up garbage from waterways. Clearbot, with headquarters in Hong Kong and India, is an electric autonomous boat scooping up trash, oil and invasive weeds from harbors. Bebot, a robot created by the Serial Cleaners, cleans up trash off beaches. If, like Paul Squibb, you pick up trash around your own community, you can use the app, Litterati, to document what you find. Litterati analyzes trash to determine if it's coming from a particular and addressable source, for example customers frequenting a certain restaurant, smokers who leave their cigarette butts on the ground, or a local factory. You can then educate people about better solutions or provide them with receptacles.

In addition to garbage clean up, other companies are focused on solving other types of damage from the Industrial Era. Startups such as AirSeed, Droneseed, Flash Forest, Mass Reforestation, and Kenya Flying Labs are using drones to help replant forests and land that have been damaged by companies, fires, floods, invasive species and pests.

In these examples, software and robots are helpful because they can perform the widespread manual labor required to clean up the extensive damage created by billions of people over the last century. While there is a lot to clean up, by partnering with robots and technology, we have a better chance of cleaning up massive messes rather than working alone.

What about climate change? Is there a way to reverse the damage done from greenhouse gases? A number of companies are building giant machines sucking carbon out of the air. The Swiss company Climeworks set up the world's first commercial carbon capture plant in Switzerland in 2017. It captures about 900 tons of carbon dioxide per year. Climework's carbon capture facility in Iceland pulls about 4000 tons of carbon from the air and they're building another facility in Iceland that can remove 36,000 tons per year. In 2023, the United States opened Heirloom Carbon Technologies, which is capable of removing about 1000 tons of carbon dioxide per year.

Carbon can also be captured in other ways. London-based Seabound, is a maritime startup capturing 95% of carbon dioxide emissions from ships. The startup Remora, is building carbon capture devices that capture emissions directly from the tailpipes of semi-trucks. Other companies, such as the Australian company Calix, and Carbon America, are building emissions capturing systems for cement and ethanol plants.

While these cleanup efforts are important, and many are in their early days yet to scale, given humans are releasing about 36 billion tons of carbon every year, we also need to radically reduce the amount of emissions going into the atmosphere in the first place. The next group of impact technology companies we will discuss are doing exactly that—overhauling and transforming our energy and transportation industries in ways that are more climate-friendly.

Greening our Existing Industries

Some of the biggest emitters of greenhouse gases are the energy, transportation, and food sectors. Earlier we took a look at innovations greening the food and agricultural industries, now let's look at the companies transforming our energy and transportation industries.

Clean energy is a big business. According to the International Energy Agency, investors poured over $1.8 trillion into the sector in 2023. While several countries such as Iceland and Paraguay are already obtaining most of their energy from renewables, huge countries and economies like the United States are also switching over faster than expected. In 2023, the United States obtained almost 40% of its electricity from renewables. China, India, and the European Union are also hitting 20-30% renewable energy each year, while Brazil is over 80%.

When we think of clean and renewable energy, we might think of solar energy, wind energy, or hydroelectric energy, but the sector also includes geothermal energy, green hydrogen, and nuclear energy. Each of these sectors in turn is creating new companies to solve specific challenges within those sectors. For example, geothermal companies need companies who can build better ways to drill into the ground. All clean energy companies need other companies to build better batteries, as well as upgrade the electricity grid so that it can handle more inputs and outputs. New software is needed to manage a grid that is more complex and vulnerable to hacking in new ways.

While nuclear fusion is still a ways off, several companies are working on it directly, and others are working on it indirectly. For example, many of the recent advances in nuclear fusion are related to the ability of super computers and artificial intelligence to understand and control the many variables needed to control ignition. As all of these different companies contribute directly or indirectly to clean energy and transportation, and are also creating many new jobs.

When you consider jobs in clean energy, keep in mind there are many different types of jobs. You might be working directly on the solution, such as by installing solar panels or repairing wind turbines, or you might be working behind the scenes. Your job might be helping a company decide what type of renewable energy or combination of energy types is best for their business given their energy usage, location, and financial constraints. Or you might work with different stakeholders in a community to set up a shared renewable energy system and plan to fund the project. You might be managing renewable energy credits, or helping a large company set up a data center powered by renewable energy. These jobs require different skill sets. Some are highly technical, while others require soft skills, such as community-organizing skills and trust building with stakeholders.

While it may make sense to continue using fossil fuels in certain industries or certain parts of the world, most of the world will transition to clean energy over the next two decades. This isn't only about solving climate change or reducing pollution. Over the long run, renewable energy will be cheaper than fossil fuels. While it will initially cost money to build renewable energy infrastructure, once that infrastructure is built, other than maintenance, the source of power—wind, sunlight, geothermal energy—is infinite and free. On the other hand, fossil fuels are limited. There's finite oil and coal in the ground, and as supplies go down, it's more expensive to extract. Renewable energy isn't only better for our health and the planet, but over the long run will be cheaper and more convenient.

As the clean energy sector continues to grow, it will create millions of jobs. In 2020, the International Energy Agency reported the number of clean energy jobs surpassed the number of fossil fuel jobs. As of 2023 over 36 million people worked in clean energy globally. According to the United States Department of Energy, in 2024 over 8 million people worked in clean energy in the United States, with the jobs in clean energy growing faster than overall job growth.

In addition to energy, one of the other biggest contributors of greenhouse gases is transportation. About 30% of greenhouse gases come from cars, trucks, ships, and airplanes moving people and goods around the planet. Transportation is a rapidly transforming industry. While certain companies like Tesla are known for their electric cars, almost every company from GE to Honda to Ford to BMW to Lamborghini, now make electric vehicles. While most of us have probably seen electric cars coast through our neighborhoods, we're also now starting to see the electrification of fleets of vehicles.

A few weeks ago, I was driving down the freeway and witnessed a whole fleet of little electric Amazon delivery trucks heading my way in the opposite lane. Perhaps 20 trucks were heading out, most likely out of a nearby Amazon warehouse on their way to start their daily deliveries. A vehicle company called Rivian is building the electric trucks for Amazon, who expects to bring 100,000 electric delivery vehicles on the road by 2030. Rivian also announced a contract to build a fleet of electric vehicles for AT&T, and has been selling electric pickup trucks to individuals for a number of years. It gives me great hope to see the electrification of commercial vehicles given how much time they spend on the roads.

When I first started my career, if you wanted to work on the challenge of climate change, you'd find yourself working for a nonprofit advocating against fossil fuel companies often protesting in the streets holding up signs. While those early climate change workers laid the foundation for the larger climate change movement, it was difficult work. The pay was terrible, and sometimes the work was dangerous or landed you in jail.

Today, if you want to stop climate change you have countless opportunities to find a job aligned with your values. If you drive an electric Amazon truck, you're part of the Climate Tech workforce. If you sell electric vehicles for a car company, you're part of the Climate Tech workforce. If you're a CEO of an electric car company, a manager, a lawyer, or work in finance at an electric vehicle company, you're part of the Climate Tech workforce. If you're retrofitting your tractor to be powered off a rechargeable battery, you're part of the Climate Tech workforce. If you're working to help large tanker ships consume less energy by using high-tech sails, such as those being developed and tested by MOL, Vale International, Wallenius Wilhelmsen, Cargill, Bar Technologies, Mitsubishi Corporation, Yara Marine Technologies, or Zéphyr & Borée, you're part of the Climate Tech workforce.

The Climate Tech workforce is even making its way into aerospace and aviation. Back in 2011, I was an early co-founder of a company called Matternet, which pioneered the drone transport industry. Our idea was to use small, electric, drones to deliver medical goods in remote, inaccessible, or congested places. This idea took off, inspiring hundreds of other startups and large companies around the world to start using commercial drones for transport. There is now an entire Air Mobility industry emerging that includes drones, air taxis, vertiports and more. Many of these drones are battery powered, meaning they can use renewable energy. Not only are they helping people access improved medical care, but they're also much better for the environment.

In addition to small transport drones, startups such as Joby Aviation, Archer Air, and Beta Technologies are building electric flying passenger taxis with vertical take-off and landing. The big companies, Boeing, Airbus, Honeywell and BAE are also building electric plane technologies. Many are also exploring other types of sustainable aviation fuels.

These companies are creating jobs not only building hardware and software infrastructure, but they need people who understand air regulations, safety issues, and legal issues. Given some of these vehicles will land in vertiports rather than runways, they need people who understand real estate, architecture, city planning, construction, and logistics.

If you head up higher into the sky, you will find even the space industry is greening. The space startup Outpost, founded by three Singularity University alumni, Jason Dunn, Aaron Kemmer, and Michael Vergalla, is building reusable satellites that deliver their payloads then fly back to Earth rather than burning up in the atmosphere. Japanese researchers at Kyoto University are experimenting with building wooden satellites that don't pollute the atmosphere upon returning to Earth.

Back on the ground, many innovators are creating electric and green boats. Norway, Finland and India already have a number of electric ferries. Natique, Candela, Pure Watercraft, and Electracraft build electric boats for recreation and fishing. Navier is building flying electric hydrofoil passenger boats.

If you want to solve climate change and save the environment, there has never been a better time to find a job. Whether you want to build electric sports cars, clean up the oceans, reimagine architecture for a world of air taxis, or help local communities make their hometowns safer and cleaner, millions of jobs are coming your way.

Responding to Climate and Natural Disasters

While it's good news companies are becoming more climate-friendly, it hasn't been fast enough. Unfortunately, many communities are now dealing with wildfires, floods, and climate catastrophes due to climate change. These disasters are inspiring a new generation of startups and companies trying to solve these problems.

Did you know hundreds of startups, companies, and individuals are working in a new field called Fire Tech? Fire Tech companies are using technology to predict and respond to all types of fires, ranging from massive wildfires and forest fires, to fires in people's homes or commercial structures. Perimeter is a startup co-founded by Bailey Farren, the daughter of emergency response workers and an evacuee of the 2017 Tubbs fire in California. Bailey realized many firefighters and emergency response workers were dealing with massive wildfires with paper maps and poor communication systems. Perimeter built an app allowing public safety officials to use a shared digital platform for evacuation management, real time data sharing, collaboration, and communicating to the public.

Another Fire Tech company, INCA, predicts the outbreak of forest fires using a combination of drones with sensors, ground sensors, and cameras. Pano AI scans landscapes for forest fires helping responders extinguish fires when they are still small. Overstory spots areas where vegetation overgrowth and power lines collide, a recipe for forest fire disasters. Kettle, also co-founded by Singularity University alumni, Nathaniel Manning, is a startup using technology to provide extremely accurate and targeted predictions for areas facing fire and natural disaster risk. It then works with homeowners to better protect their property, as well as reinsurance companies.

More broadly, robotics companies like Boston Dynamics have built dog-like robots that can venture into disaster areas assessing damage or searching for injured people. Drones are now commonly used to search for and help victims of earthquakes, floods, hurricanes, tornadoes, and other disasters. Earlier we discussed how NVIDIA is building a digital twin of our planet to track climate change. One can also build a digital twin of a city, and run simulations for what might happen, and how to best respond, if there's a flood or earthquake.

The number of jobs emerging in the Climate Tech and Green Tech workforce is staggering. Terra.do is an online platform for climate workers with 44,000 open jobs and a goal of helping 100 million people find climate jobs by 2030. In this chapter, we have covered companies working in food, transportation, renewable energy, and disaster response, but there are countless other types of jobs focused on climate, sustainability, and the environment. Many medium and large-sized companies are now hiring Chief Sustainability Officers and sustainability teams to track and manage their company's carbon emissions, water pollution, air pollution, supply chains, and recycling efforts. Banks, investors, family offices, venture capital firms, and philanthropists are hiring teams to invest in and fund startups and organizations solving climate change or healing the planet. If you are looking for an impact technology job, clean energy, climate, and sustainability are great places to start.

CHAPTER 6—CLASSROOM IN THE CLOUD: THE ED TECH WORKFORCE

When I was in graduate school, I worked at an educational nonprofit in Myanmar, the country in Southeast Asia also known as Burma. My job was to help 20 Burmese high school students find internships at local nonprofits to gain work experience. At the time, Myanmar was at the top of the list for everything gone wrong. It was one of the poorest countries globally, had one of the world's worst education systems, and was suffering from civil wars, corruption, the drug trade, and every complication you could imagine. When I arrived, the country's pro-Democracy leader, Aung San Suu Kyi, was under house arrest and the entire country was under economic sanctions from the United States. While I was legally allowed to travel to Myanmar, I wasn't allowed to spend money on items other than necessities such as food and shelter. While it was a difficult country to work in, I went because I believed if I could help those 20 students, they could later help others in their country. While most people thought I was being idealistic and naïve to try to make a difference, I thought to myself, "Why not try?"

If you have been to Myanmar, you will know it's a country of contrasts. It's a place of great beauty and great suffering. I remember landing at the airport to see lush, green, trees, and tropical jungle-like vegetation dispersed throughout the city. Amidst the greenery were clusters of tall, glowing, golden temples, part of Myanmar's Buddhist culture and history. It was a breathtakingly beautiful and magical place.

Yet I also remember walking down the streets horrified by Myanmar's education system. I would walk past a school, which was often a single classroom crammed with several different grades of children and hear a cacophony of noise emerging. The teachers had written lessons on the chalkboard for the children to recite by rote, and each grade level was repeating what the teacher wrote at the top of their lungs. Because different grade levels, with different lessons, were all in one classroom, no one could hear anything. I was surprised anyone could learn in such an environment and also concerned kids were still learning by rote, when most of the world had shifted to student-centered teaching and active learning.

Things were much worse for the poorer children. One day, I visited an orphanage that housed kids whose parents had passed away, as well as kids whose parents couldn't afford to keep them. The orphanage was located in an empty structure that resembled a dilapidated parking garage. Young kids, who appeared to have never had a bath or a good meal in their lives, were living together in a mob in a darkened corner of the structure. I visited this group of kids with some of my older high school students and they said the children were so isolated and neglected they had invented their own language. After I visited the kids, I developed a rash across my stomach.

It's easy to lose hope after experiences such as these. What chance would any of these kids have? Not only were they growing up in poverty without proper food, clothing, shelter, or healthcare, on top of that, they would hardly be able to communicate with other people. How would they ever be able to go to school if they had the chance? How would they ever get a job?

Myanmar, like many war-torn and impoverished countries, did have people trying to make things better. For decades, well-funded humanitarian organizations, foreign governments, nonprofits, and global experts had tried various interventions to improve the education system. However, most of them failed, or only helped a few people.

Then things changed. In 2015, I reconnected with Hla Hla Win, one of my former high school students in Myanmar. Hla Hla was now a teacher in Myanmar and setting up a school to train teachers in student-centered teaching methods. I encouraged her to apply to Singularity University's startup program to further support her efforts and she was accepted. She won a scholarship to cover the cost of the program, and crowd-funded her plane ticket to Silicon Valley. She had a one-year-old daughter whom she left in Myanmar with her husband and family for several months. No matter what, Hla Hla was determined to improve the education system.

While Hla Hla was an avid video game player, she had no formal training in technology. Despite that, upon arriving in Silicon Valley, within 10 weeks she quickly learned about software, computing, virtual reality, and augmented reality. After completing the program, Hla Hla returned to Myanmar, and in collaboration with her husband, launched 360 Ed, one of the first Ed Tech companies in Myanmar. While Hla Hla was planning to train teachers, she realized she could help more students if she reached them directly. 360 Ed uses augmented reality to make super fun and interactive content where kids learn vocabulary, science, math and more. It also works offline, given power outages are frequent in Myanmar, and comes in multiple languages, given Myanmar's diversity. 360 Ed's learning applications seemed a dream come true compared to the rote-based education system I had seen in Myanmar a few years earlier. Even more astonishing, her solution was equivalent to or better than what many kids had access to in Silicon Valley at the time.

Hla Hla's timing in launching her startup was impeccable. Myanmar had its first democratic government in decades and many people had smartphones and tablets. 360 Ed took off, successfully reaching hundreds of thousands of kids, teachers and parents. Hla Hla had hired over 60 staff, giving workers some of their first jobs working at a technology startup. She also hired hundreds of salespeople around the country improving local lives and economies.

Hla Hla didn't stop there. As an impact technology

entrepreneur, she wanted to inspire other entrepreneurs to solve problems in her country and build the local innovation ecosystem. She started collaborating with universities, helping college students learn about impact technology. She set up a maker space for the community where people could visit and try new technologies firsthand. She helped business leaders learn about investing in technology startups. Soon, a nascent innovation system emerged.

As 360 Ed began to succeed, educators and innovators from around the world, including many in other low-income countries, came to visit Myanmar hoping to replicate Hla Hla's work in their own countries. 360 Ed also began winning global awards. Hla Hla also secured a contract with the democratic government in Myanmar to digitize and upgrade the entire nation's education system. After decades of no progress, a schoolteacher, with no technology background, but a lot of determination, began overturning one of the world's worst education systems by launching an Ed Tech startup.

Then things fell apart. The county's military dictatorship, in the midst of an already trying time during the pandemic, launched a *coup d'état* after losing an election. War and violence broke out across the country. My friends in Myanmar were sharing social media videos of explosions outside their homes and soldiers gunning down people in the streets. Because Hla Hla was influential in Myanmar, the military government put her on a wanted list, and she had to go in and out of hiding while trying to take care of her family and the company. At the same time, the military government was turning the Internet on and off and shutting down the banking system, making it impossible for businesses to sell their products or pay their staff. Hla Hla fled to a local temple to hide, devastated, believing all was lost.

Then something remarkable happened. Hla Hla saw that the young children who were also hiding in the temple were using 360 Ed offline to continue learning, despite the war and pandemic raging outside. Although her company was in chaos, and her future uncertain, the technology survived. The kids were learning. Globally, one of the biggest reasons children drop out of school is because of war and conflict. Hla Hla, a teacher-turned-tech-entrepreneur, who herself grew up in a land of war and conflict, had found a solution that actually worked.

Over the next two years Hla Hla, her family, and many of her staff fled Myanmar and relocated to the United States, Thailand, India and other countries where they worked remotely in safer environments. Step by step, they rebuilt the company, even releasing new products while on the run. 360 Ed now serves nearly one million children within Myanmar, the United States, and around the world, with its products available on Walmart and Amazon.

Hla Hla's story is a striking example of resilience, as well as how impact technology companies can help millions of children living in the worst circumstances. If you are interested in working in Ed Tech, you can make a difference in children's lives that can last for generations. Even if you live in a lower-income country, you can find a job working in this sector, or start your own company. As next generation satellite networks make the Internet more affordable and accessible, there are opportunities to reach billions of kids who previously had no education or only access to poor education systems.

Today, Ed Tech is a huge field. According to Grandview Research, the global Ed Tech market was valued at $142 billion in 2023 and will continue growing. The first Ed Tech initiatives emerged in the 2000s and primarily involved established universities broadcasting their existing classes to people on the Internet for free. Today, Ed Tech is filled with learning opportunities for people of all ages and backgrounds.

There are countless companies building fun, education-based, games for kids teaching a wide variety of subjects in every language. There are companies like Key2Enable, a Brazilian startup that was also part of Singularity University, building technology that empowers people with different mental and physical abilities to access computers, for example with eye movements or short hand movements on specially designed keyboards. There are avatar tutors powered by artificial intelligence that will guide you through your lessons in a personalized way. There are companies building content for home-schooled children and companies building software systems for entire school districts. There are new types of professional trainings for doctors, pilots, and automotive workers that harness virtual reality. There are online classes for people pursuing hobbies or sports. Ed Tech is unlimited in its potential. People always want to learn more, and there is always more to learn.

Given education works best when it's fun and engaging, the education industry and entertainment industries are also merging into the Edutainment field. Another founder I met at Singularity University, an Italian actress-turned-entrepreneur, Lucrezia Bisignani, founded Kukua, a successful Edutainment company that originated in Africa and is now global. Lucrezia started her company after spending time with kids in schools across villages in different African countries. She wanted to create educational content that would be educational as well as inspiring. While many kids now have access to educational technologies, Lucrezia believed they needed more. She believed kids need to be inspired to learn by seeing how they can use what they learn in their own lives and futures. Based on her time in the villages, Lucrezia created Super Sema, Africa's first animated superhero cartoon. Super Sema is a young African girl who uses STEAM skills (Science, Technology, Engineering, Art, Math), to save the world. Super Sema now includes three animated series watched by over 140 million kids worldwide, as well as educational songs, games, learning kits, toys, books and more. Kukua's goal is to help kids learn, but also develop the confidence to become makers, creators and technology innovators.

Lucrezia didn't build her company alone. She works with a team in East Africa and several powerful black women in Hollywood including Lupita Nyong'o, who is a shareholder in the company and executive producer of the animated series. In this sense, Kukua is not only educating kids, but also creating jobs in East

Africa and helping Hollywood reimage itself in a changing world. While many in Hollywood are fearful artificial intelligence will steal their jobs, Kukua is showing a different way forward, one where entrepreneurs, actresses and producers are making the most of the technology, not being displaced by it.

While many are working on Ed Tech initiatives to support kids, others are working on solutions for adults. Another founder I met at Singularity University, Muriel Claussen Closs, co-founded a company called AnthillAI. Muriel observed that while many white-collar workers have access to on the-job-trainings at their desks or through in-person trainings, deskless workers are being left behind. Deskless workers are the workers who sit behind steering wheels and cash registers or are on their feet all day working in hospitals or construction sites or performing other jobs that require them to be away from desks. AnthillAI reaches deskless workers by helping employers communicate, coach, and train workers through whatever device they have access to, and in over 75 languages. Now that many companies are incorporating artificial intelligence into their businesses, AnthillAI also works to empower front line workers to co-create how these technologies are used. Imagine a world where every worker has access to professional development services and advanced technologies in the way most convenient and helpful to them. As technology becomes more sophisticated, and as costs continue to fall, we can design systems helping workers from all backgrounds and sectors thrive and grow.

Are you interested in joining the Ed Tech workforce? Could you see yourself helping kids and adults learn about a variety of topics? Let's talk about the specific jobs available in Ed Tech and what Ed Tech workers do. At a high level, most Ed Tech companies, whether they're serving children or adults, need people to build their digital products, sell their products, improve their products, as well as operate the overall company.

What is an Ed Tech product? An Ed Tech product might be an online education course, an online video game that incorporates learning, an educational movie, a digital tutor, a virtual coach, a system to manage online learning for a school or company, a program that helps schools manage grades, and more. A product is usually created by someone who creates the content, such as the actual course content or the script of the video, a designer who considers the presentation of the content to the students, and engineers who build the product with computer code. Sometimes artists, actors, and actresses are also involved. Given that a lot of different people create a product, a product manager usually oversees the entire project.

Products can be built to work alone with students or in collaboration with a teacher or facilitator. There are also jobs for people who track the impact of the product, such as learning outcomes. Today, learning outcomes are often tracked digitally, and products can track how fast students are progressing through their lessons and offer feedback and select the next best lesson for them depending on what they need. This information can also help a teacher manage an entire class or a principal to manage a school.

Ed Tech companies also need employees who sell products, run demonstrations for customers, track what competing companies are building, and ensure products are aligned with local and national teaching guidelines and regulations. Given some Ed Tech companies are startups, they also need employees raising money from investors. Like many impact technology industries, the Ed Tech sector includes jobs from the past as well as new ones.

The Ed Tech industry is also in a great deal of flux. As the world of work changes, teachers and parents wonder what kids need to learn to be prepared for the future. During the pandemic, many parents homeschooled their children and some continued the practice after the pandemic ended. More adults are returning to school launching second careers. Artificial intelligence is also transforming education.

Another innovator I met through Singularity University, Brainy Swaibu, is a teacher and founder of Spectrum Transformative Services, a community-based organization and school located at a refugee settlement on the border of Uganda and Congo. While

Brainy and his students struggle in meeting many of their basic needs, such as proper shelter, they're using artificial intelligence to supplement their curriculum and create a strategic plan to grow the school into a university and job creation innovation hub that transforms the refugee settlement.

Brainy also teaches his students digital literacy. Digital literacy helps students think through questions such as how accurate artificial intelligence is, or how one should balance learning for one's self versus outsourcing their thinking to an artificial intelligence.

Whether you're a teacher working in a wealthy urban city in the United States or Europe, or whether you're a teacher working in a refugee settlement in Uganda, helping kids understand how to navigate artificial intelligence and other new technologies is now of utmost importance and a global challenge. If you're interested in Ed Tech, you can forge a fascinating career using technology to help individual students learn and improve their lives, as well as serve on the front lines of grappling with some of the bigger, existential questions facing our education systems and future.

CHAPTER 7—GOOD HEALTH FOR ALL: THE HEALTH TECH WORKFORCE

When war broke out in Ukraine, I received a message from some Singularity University alumni living inside the country. They wanted to know if I knew of anyone who could help an eight-year-old girl who had her arm shot off during the war, access a high-tech prosthetic arm. I reached out to my network and Singularity University's co-founder, Peter Diamandis, referred me to a startup called Unlimited Tomorrow that was building low-cost bionic arms and was interested in helping. Soon, a group of us had hatched a plan to help the young girl as well as other patients who had lost limbs in Ukraine. We set up a crowdfunder and, thanks to the help of many generous individuals and companies, were able to get to work.

As we set off to help various victims, I was astonished by how much the world, and healthcare, had changed during the pandemic and how those changes transformed not only healthcare, but our ability to help people living in war zones. For most of my life, and throughout human history, if you wanted to help someone in a war zone, there wasn't much you could do that would make a difference. You could donate items or money, and perhaps advocate for peace, but you were dependent on large governments or humanitarian organizations to help directly. Even when humanitarian groups entered a country, they could often only help a few people in limited ways, working with extremely limited resources in dangerous conditions. If you were an injured victim inside a war zone, it might take years to find help and you might need to leave your country making a dangerous journey as a refugee.

Technology is changing everything. For our project helping patients in Ukraine, we worked remotely with teams of people and patients working around the world, most who had never met in person. Once a patient was identified, a local medical team in Ukraine would scan images of that person's remaining arm, and what was left of the lost arm. Initially, Unlimited Tomorrow mailed them a scanner, but in a pinch, they could use a smartphone camera. Then the medical team in Ukraine emailed the images back to Unlimited Tomorrow, based in the United States. Unlimited Tomorrow then 3D printed several sockets (soft sleeves that help connect the prosthetic to the person's body) and eventually, the bionic arm, which was customized to fit the patient's size, shape, skin tone and more. Initially we shipped these items through the mail with the help of Singularity University alumni delivering packages in the region, but they could have also been printed on local printers (in fact, once our project took off, several groups launched similar projects inside Ukraine, scaling up the idea.)

While helping the patient obtain an arm was an important step, the second step was helping the patient learn how to use the arm and engage in physical training. The patients completed this work via tele-health and video sessions. This process took place in weeks rather than years. Only a few years ago, if you were in a war zone, it would take years to access a prosthetic, and it might not work well. Today, patients can receive them on demand, customized, and anywhere in the world. Because bionic arms are made of software and technology, they also fall in cost, making them increasingly affordable. Our work was led by a startup and a group of volunteers who simply wanted to help. Imagine what large, well-funded companies, governments, and hospitals might be able to accomplish with today's technology. As the cost of 3D printers and medical devices fall, as surgical robots spread around the world, and as the Internet and renewable energy becomes ubiquitous, we should be able to help everyone on the planet who needs access to healthcare.

Do you want to work in Health Tech and be part of building this future? We are seeing more ways than ever, for individuals, startups, and large companies, to bring healthcare to all, even in the most unlikely of places.

Helping Burned Out Doctors and Nurses

If you work as a doctor, nurse or in any role within our healthcare system, you're likely severely burned out. While part of this has to do with the pandemic, many workers are also leaving healthcare because it's simply too stressful and understaffed.

What if there was a way to get our healthcare workers more support, as well as help patients better manage their health, preventing some of the worst and most expensive healthcare crises? Or what if there was a way to help billions of people living in underserved or rural regions around the world access high-quality healthcare?

Dr. Sanjeev Arora set up Project Echo in 2003 to solve this problem. As a doctor working in New Mexico, a rural land where many people drive hours to visit the doctor, he realized thousands of people were suffering from Hepatitis C that could have been cured if caught earlier. Sanjeev asked himself, "what if we could help these patients access healthcare by moving knowledge rather than people?"

Project Echo began training rural healthcare workers with the specialist skills needed to treat Hepatitis C locally, and demonstrated their patients had the same outcomes as patients who traveled to the state's top medical centers.

Today, Project Echo has trained and mentored nearly 5.5 million doctors, nurses, and healthcare workers in rural and underserved areas in over 200 countries across a variety of healthcare conditions. Over 600 peer-reviewed articles have documented the success of their work. By providing more healthcare workers with high-quality training, Project Echo is not only reaching patients who lack access to medical care completely, but is also helping alleviate the tremendous pressure faced by burned out doctors and nurses.

The Project Echo model works by bringing together local healthcare workers and specialists through tele-mentoring and knowledge sharing to review and discuss different cases together. By moving knowledge, rather than people, they believe they can provide anyone on our planet with the care they need. I think of Project Echo as the "medical school" of the future, where healthcare workers anywhere, can be trained in anything, as needed.

Consider the other changes happening in healthcare. Imagine Project Echo's work complemented by new wearable sensors and monitoring devices that can detect medical problems in advance, new types of robots that can perform surgeries, medical drones that can improve the logistics and delivery of lab tests and medicine, and 3D printers and bioreactors that can print supplies and grow therapeutics on demand, anytime, anywhere. It's not just knowledge that we can now move, but someday, entire hospitals and pharmacies.

Lowering the Cost of Treatment

One of the biggest challenges in healthcare is cost. But what if we could radically lower the cost of healthcare? One of the leading innovators addressing this challenge is Dr. Mary Lou Jepson. Mary Lou became interested in this challenge after two life-changing experiences. First, as a college student, she discovered she had a brain tumor. While her tumor was successfully treated, she was shocked by how expensive and inaccessible it was to get medical scans—an important technology for identifying and monitoring her tumor. Later, Mary Lou became co-founder and Chief Technology Officer of One Laptop Per Child. The goal of One Laptop Per Child was to lower the cost of computers from $1000 to $100, a price point that would make laptops and education software accessible to millions of children around the world. Given her experience in building low-cost computers, Mary

Lou later set out to lower the cost of expensive medical imaging equipment.

In 2016, she founded OpenWater, which started with the goal of lowering the cost of MRI images and today has built a wearable head device that uses ultrasound and infrared light to treat a wide variety of diseases. While ultrasound and infrared light have been around for many years, OpenWater realized they can use software to precisely control the sound and light making them useful for more purposes. For example, they can steer beams of light and create harmonics that can destroy cancer cells and avoid healthy cells. They have found that as they destroy cancer cells, the cancer gives off a protein that vaccinates surrounding cells from that specific cancer. They're testing this application in human trials. OpenWater has also successfully treated depression in people with their device. When they aim at certain neurons, they can turn neurons on and off and encourage them to release neurotransmitters. It's possible OpenWater's device will replace the need for surgery and drugs in treating certain ailments. OpenWater believes their device will also be able to help with strokes, seizures, migraine, addiction, neurodegenerative diseases, inflammation and more. They're even referring to it as a Silicon Hospital—imagine one wearable, portable, device that can treat many different diseases, all without surgery and drugs.

If that's not enough, Mary Lou is determined that her work will help everyone. In 2024 she announced that in addition to raising $54 million from investors, she has made her work open source. This means that she will license it to anyone for free. The solutions can reach more people at an affordable price, and scientists and innovators around the world can use the platform to tackle diseases in their expertise. While many researchers have been experimenting with ultrasound and infrared light over the last few years, most of them never developed and commercialized their solutions because it was too expensive.

Having access to open-source technology and a collaborative platform will lower costs and allow more new treatments to succeed, especially given that anyone using the platform agrees to share their safety data. *Time Magazine* named Mary Lou one of the world's 100 most influential people.

Helping Everyone

While OpenWater and Project Echo are creating solutions that can help billions of people, other innovators are working on helping patients who have been overlooked by today's healthcare systems. Qvin, a Fem Tech company started by two founders from Denmark, Dr. Sara Naseri and Søren Therkelsen, whom I met at Singularity University, recently received FDA clearance to launch their smart menstrual pads. Qvin's founders realized that billions of women could avoid having to go to the doctor's office to have their blood drawn with needles if healthcare workers could instead analyze the blood they naturally lose each month during their periods. They realized needle blood draws had been invented by men, who had overlooked this other source of blood that was much easier, cheaper, and less painful to collect.

After several years of research, Qvin proved they can successfully use menstrual blood for medical tests and released their first product, an A1c test, which measures blood sugar and is widely used to test for and manage diabetes and pre-diabetes. Their tests are simple and easy to use. One simply pulls out an insert from their menstrual pad and mails it to the lab. Qvin is also developing a number of other tests that can work with their smart menstrual pad. In addition to Qvin, there are thousands of other startups now working in Fem Tech. They're tackling challenges related to women's health, pregnancy, childbirth, menopause, and hormonal issues.

While Qvin, OpenWater and Project Echo are examples of Health Tech companies dramatically improving healthcare, they're a sampling of tens of thousands of companies and startups working in healthcare. The entire global healthcare industry is digitizing and transforming itself. All of us will be impacted by these changes. Whether it's artificial intelligence helping find new antibiotics and cures for cancer, personalized medicine creating individual treatments for patients based on their genetics and lifestyle, breakthroughs in longevity, digital healthcare records that make information sharing easier, online access to mental health counseling, or robots performing surgeries, healthcare is reinventing itself.

If you're interested in healthcare careers, I would direct you to a few resources that provide a bird's-eye perspective of the many changes happening. My former colleague, Dr. Daniel Kraft, founded NextMed Health, which hosts an annual conference on the future of healthcare. He works closely with Shawna Butler, RN MBA, a nurse economist leading a movement to empower nurses to serve as leaders in healthcare innovation and entrepreneurship. Their conference covers a wide range of topics from the role of Generative AI in medicine, to startups working to cure rare diseases, to augmented reality in healthcare, to new types of imaging devices, to synthetic biology to breakthroughs in women's health.

Another former colleague, Robin Farmanfarmaian, has written several books including *The Patient as CEO,* which covers Health Tech from the perspective of the patient. Another former colleague, Andrew Hessell, in collaboration with futurist Amy Webb, recently published *The Genesis Machine: Our Quest to Rewrite Life in the Age of Synthetic Biology.* Synthetic biology refers to editing or rewriting our DNA code. In addition to health applications, synthetic biology has applications in agriculture, food, material science and more. Their book explores both the opportunities and risks presented by this technology.

Another founder I met at Singularity University, Juan Francisco Llamazares, from Argentina, is the co-founder of a company called Stämm. Stämm has invented a new type of bioreactor that can efficiently grow cells for therapeutics at scale, and in the future can also grow lab-grown food and other materials. While Stämm is initially working in healthcare, their long-term goal is to replace 60% of all "man-made" objects on our planet with bio-grown materials.

Today, we live in a world where our food, healthcare, clothing, fuel and other industries are all separate. Over time, we might have new industries emerge that can work across all these sectors. Just as Dr. Mary Lou Jepsen is building an open-source hardware and software platform that can work across many diseases, Stämm is building hardware and software that can work across multiple industries.

What does this mean for the future of work? While we'll always need specialists, we'll also need people who can work across multiple industries. We need people who work at the convergence of different fields and problems. We need people who can creatively see the linkages and opportunities across many systems, and who are willing to try out new solutions and work in unconventional ways.

Keep this in mind as you consider future careers in impact technology industries. You may currently be working in healthcare and have the perfect background to transition into the future of food or lab-grown sustainable fuels for jets. Likewise, you may work in sustainable aviation fuels, or lab-grown proteins, and could be a valuable asset to a startup working in healthcare.

CHAPTER 8—A MORE PEACEFUL AND JUST WORLD: THE TECHNOLOGY FOR GOOD WORKFORCE

So far we have explored impact technology companies solving problems in food, agriculture, climate, environment, education, and healthcare. Guess what? This is just the tip of the iceberg and there are many more impact technology companies and industries out there. Let's do a quick dive into Housing and Construction Tech, advanced manufacturing, cybersecurity, the ethics of technology, Gov Tech, and Peace Tech—all rapidly growing sectors.

The Housing Crisis

Housing is a huge challenge in nearly every country in the world. According to the United Nations, over 1.6 billion people lack adequate housing. Countries such as Somalia, Egypt, Pakistan, Kenya, the Philippines, and Mexico, each have millions of people living in slums, yet you can also find hundreds of thousands of people living on the streets or in their vehicles in the United States. Around the world, millions of refugees live in tents and shelters vulnerable to poor weather, or are on the move without housing at all. If you lack housing, you are also likely to suffer from other social problems, such as poor health and safety challenges.

Different people face housing challenges for different reasons. Some people lack access to employment or credit, while others live in areas of extreme economic inequality, making housing expensive. In other places families are driven from their homes by war, violence, or natural disasters. Certain countries are riddled with corruption and lack adequate property rights and protections. At an individual level, people may have lost their housing due to bad luck or acute situations, such as a lost job, domestic violence, a divorce, a death in the family, a major health crisis, or a struggle with addiction.

How do we solve the global housing crisis given how complex the problem is? Around the world, startups and companies are tackling different parts of the problem using different solutions. Miracle Messages, founded by Singularity University alumni Kevin Adler, helps connect unhoused people to friends and relatives who are searching for them. The WIN App and Shelter App connect vulnerable people to housing and other resources. Entidad helps farm workers, a group known to struggle with housing challenges, digitally access support services. DigitalTolk, a Swedish company co-founded by a Singularity University alumni, Virpal Singh, provides on demand translation helping vulnerable groups such as refugees access help.

The company, iBuild, based in the United States, Kenya, Mexico and India, is trying to make housing more affordable by creating an efficient marketplace for the construction industries. They unite customers who have a construction project with contractors, workers, suppliers, engineers, architects, lenders, insurance companies, government agencies, and other relevant players, all in one place. Another company, DeepBlocks, founded by Olivia Ramos, whom I also met at Singularity University, has built software that lets developers analyze zoning requirements and costs and then projects financial returns for new construction projects.

A number of companies are building gigantic 3D printers to print houses at a fraction of the time and cost as traditional homes. A for profit and nonprofit company, Icon and New Story, have already printed homes in the United States and Mexico, including for people who were formerly unhoused. The Danish company COBOD, constructed the first 3D printed house in Europe. Construction 3D is a French company building 3D printers for the construction industry. 3D printers can also help with roads, bridges, and smaller structures such as public bathrooms, a huge problem in many low-income countries.

While these 3D printers are still expensive, there is hope that over time they will be able to significantly bring down prices. Other impact technology companies are focusing on greening the construction industry, creating more energy efficient buildings, manufacturing low-emission green concrete, or reusing recycled wood. The New America Foundation is using digital technologies to address the challenge of abandoned buildings, false property sales, and land rights in parts of the world where traditional records are not kept.

The Housing Tech and Construction industries are closely related to the robotics and advanced manufacturing industries. Globally, factories around the world are working to automate every industry and create robots that can build anything and everything. While robotics and advanced manufacturing require billions in investment, once these industries are mature, they will have a profound impact on the world and our economy. Robots can supply us with many of our basic needs, from housing, to transportation, to medicine, to food, to clothing. Robots can also build other robots, further lowering costs and speeding up development.

While robots and advanced manufacturing can create technological unemployment and economic inequality, if a region is able to help workers develop new skills, and offer incentives that ensure consumers benefit from robots through lower prices or stock ownership in robotics companies, they can play a huge role in improving people's lives and uplifting economies.

One company working to advance automation while also creating jobs is Re:Build Manufacturing, which is working to digitize and modernize the United States manufacturing industry. They work across industrial equipment, aerospace, defense, healthcare, Climate Tech and more with the specific goal of creating jobs and rebuilding communities by harnessing automation. As automation spreads around the world, it's essential that we roll it out in ways that also create jobs and benefit consumers.

Cybersecurity and the Ethics of Technology

Given the tumultuous state of politics and polarization happening around the world, and given the role of social media and technology-driven fake news, I wouldn't blame you if you feel technology is ruining democracy and governance. Some politicians, governments and nefarious gangs are using advanced technologies to undermine and destabilize legitimate governments. If that's not enough, most of us have probably come across online criminals and hackers using technology to trick us into giving away money or simply ruining our peace of mind with relentless messages and scams. While I wish people had seen these problems in advance, and built safeguards into the technology, the best we can do now is repair the damage that has been done, and find ways to do better in the future. If you are interested in these topics, you might explore careers in cybersecurity, and the ethics and regulation of technology.

The profession of cybersecurity has been around for decades. While initially only large governments and companies needed cybersecurity, today, because technology is everywhere, and because it's sophisticated and powerful, everyone needs help with cybersecurity. Hackers and criminals have gone from sending phishing scams over email to threatening anything connected to the Internet. Everything from our cars to our electricity grids to our medical devices must now be protected. Over five million people work in cybersecurity today and we can expect more jobs as we digitize more and more aspects of our lives.

While cybersecurity is aimed at stopping hackers and people purposefully abusing technology, we also need people working on the ethics and regulation of technology to prevent unintended consequences. There are many people building and using technology who are not setting out to harm others, but just haven't imagined what could go wrong. For example, artificial intelligence might help overworked teachers in the classroom, yet we don't know how interacting with artificial intelligence might impact children's minds. Aerial drones can be used to rescue lost hikers in the wilderness, or your neighbor can use them to spy on you. Neurotechnologies, or devices that can sense our brain activity or connect directly to our brains, can help people who are paralyzed or facing certain diseases, yet to some extent can also read people's minds and are a threat to our privacy.

Almost all new technologies come with risks, and we need people who can understand and consider these risks, articulate them, and come up with solutions to mitigate them. If you are interested in this topic, there are a lot of jobs emerging in the ethics and regulation of technology. These jobs can range from being a Chief Ethics Officer at a large company, to serving as an ethical advisor to startups, to working for think tanks or humanitarian organizations, to working as a lawyer or policymaker involved in crafting regulations for governments or other groups.

While some people working in these jobs are formally trained in ethics, philosophy, law, or regulations, others are employees who simply saw the need to think about these issues and convinced their bosses to create new roles in their existing companies or organizations.

Gov Tech and Peace Tech

Two other fields related to the governance of technology are Gov Tech and Peace Tech. Gov Tech involves helping governments better use technology to serve citizens. One of my colleagues from Matternet, Paola Santana, is tackling the challenge of improving governance and procurement. Her company Social Glass, streamlines and simplifies procurement, while also connecting small businesses to government buyers. Along the way, governments and citizens gain better insight into how they're spending their money and what they're prioritizing.

Another interesting Gov Tech leader is the Government of

Estonia. Over the last few years, Estonia has digitized almost all aspects of governance and social services from voting to healthcare to education. They built a system where citizens own their data and decide who to share it with, rather than the government owning everyone's data in a centralized system. As many countries around the world digitize public services, decisions such as who controls data will have a big impact on how democratic that country is down the road. Helping governments digitize their services today can be a powerful way to help tomorrow's citizens live good lives.

Peace Tech is another new impact technology field. A number of startups are building life-saving technology for people living in war zones, transforming what it means to be a civilian in a war. The startup, Hala Systems, built a way to track incoming jets and weapons based on acoustics and crowdsourcing and uses that information to provide warnings to civilians, hospitals and schools. PeachTech Labs builds technology for combating misinformation and hate speech. Other Peace Tech efforts help nonprofits and people living in conflict zones access technology to improve humanitarian aid or build other solutions to improve their own circumstance.

As you can see, the impact technology field is vast. Impact technology companies are working on almost every problem in every country, ranging from small organizations providing education to refugees to large global companies building electric cars and satellites. While hopefully this book has helped you learn about some of the impact technology jobs you might be interested in, another topic to consider is how to successfully transition into your future career. Do you want to move to the other side of the world and work at a small startup helping people access clean water? Do you want to work remotely for a large, stable, company in an established impact technology industry? Do you want to start your own company? In the next few chapters, we'll explore some of the different paths you can take based on what career you're most interested in and what level of risk and change is right for you.

PART III

*GET YOUR IMPACT
TECHNOLOGY JOB*

CHAPTER 9—FIND YOUR CONFIDENCE: YOU HAVE THE SKILLS YOU NEED

N ow that we have explored some of the new impact technology industries and companies, let's turn to you and discuss how you can get a job with one of these companies. While these jobs might seem interesting and fascinating to you, your first thought might be that you don't have the skills and background required for one of these jobs. Guess what? Because impact technology companies are new, hardly anyone has the skills and background necessary to work for them.

A different way of thinking about these jobs is how your existing skills will transfer over to them, and how you can learn on the job, once you get there. However, even before we dive into that topic, it's important to discuss how you can find your courage and confidence to change jobs in the first place. If you don't believe you can get a job, you will never try, or you will try, and give up at the first sign of trouble. You will then be stuck in the same situation, or perhaps even worse, feeling completely helpless to change your future.

Instead you have to deeply believe that you can be part of the impact technology revolution and the future jobs coming your way. You have to believe you have something important to contribute, and that you are capable of doing so.

In the upcoming pages, I will share how I found the courage and confidence to make significant career changes at different stages in my life, and what I learned along the way.

Finding Your Courage and Confidence

Over the course of my life, I've had a wide range of jobs offering both positive and negative experiences. In high school, I worked in fast food service. In college and early in my career, I had jobs ranging from data entry, to working as a receptionist, to painting houses. One time I even worked for a library removing staples from documents. I've also worked as an event planner, a fundraiser, a housing coordinator, an exchange student program manager, an English teacher, in marketing, program management, operations, partnership management, as a faculty member, as a Vice President and as a co-founder of my own companies. Over the years I've taken jobs I didn't want just to pay the bills, have been underemployed, and have worked in toxic cultures. I've been laid off or worked for years for companies or organizations that were financially unstable. I've also been in jobs where I loved what I did every day, had inspiring colleagues, and was paid well for my contributions. More often than not, I worked in jobs that offered a mixed bag of experiences. During my career, I have also made huge career switches, taking big risks to jump into new industries in which I was never formally trained.

When I look back at my career, I'm proud of what I have accomplished and believe I helped solve some important social and environmental problems. However, while it all looks good in retrospect, it wasn't always fun or easy along the way. Over the course of my life, I've applied for and been rejected from hundreds of jobs. When I was working in the nonprofit sector, I had to volunteer for several months to get myself an entry-level job, for which I was overqualified, while I worked side jobs during the evenings and weekends to pay my bills. When I worked at startups, for other organizations, or for myself, I would often face rejection while looking for grants, funding, or contracts. Because I worked on some very ambitious projects, I regularly encountered criticism, often on a daily basis.

Most people I know, even extremely successful people, have similar stories. Careers are rarely straightforward and easy. Consider that around the world, billions of people are in jobs they hate, are underemployed, or have dropped out of the workforce entirely. Why? Sometimes people live in circumstances where there are no jobs available. Other times, better jobs are available, but people don't know about them. Quite often, however, people don't bother to change jobs because it involves fear, uncertainty and rejection. You might think it's better to be in a job you hate, that undervalues and underpays you, rather than risk having no job at all, or going through a job search process that destroys the little confidence you have left. So how do you find your courage and confidence to make a change?

At different times in my life, I've found my courage and confidence in different ways. Early in my career, when I faced professional rejection, I did one thing. I kept going no matter what. Why? There was no alternative. I needed a job to survive, and I just kept trying. I would do work I hated, live as cheaply as I could, and look for something better.

During those times, I was vulnerable. Sometimes I was working with a good team and manager, and other times I was in a toxic environment. My confidence would go up and down depending on my work environment or a thoughtless comment dropped by a colleague or supervisor. Part of the challenge of a bad work environment is it eats away at what little confidence you have, making it harder to find the courage to find something better. Later in my career, I learned to find my confidence from within, rather than from my work environment or other people. I didn't learn this until I was in my mid-30s, and I learned it by taking a huge risk.

One time, after working for several years for an organization where I felt like there was no opportunity for growth, I read an article in a newspaper about a program teaching people how to use technology to solve social problems at a place called Singularity University. I applied but received a notification that I was rejected and put on a waitlist. Disappointed, I tried to not let the feeling of rejection impact me, and moved on with my life. However, a few weeks later, I received another message stating that I had made it off the waitlist. Furthermore, I had received a scholarship for the program, and needed to move across the country and start the program in two days.

While I wanted to attend the program, it meant taking a huge risk. I had always been an extremely responsible person, and had trouble imagining leaving a job on two-days notice, and passing on my unfinished work so unexpectedly to my colleagues. I was also afraid that if I left my job, I might not be able to find another job after the program ended.

While I was terrified, I also felt a fire of certainty burning within me. I was going, no matter what! I would find a way to make it work. I went to my boss and made a case that I had four weeks of unused vacation, could work remotely, and that what I learned during the program about new technologies could benefit the organization. For reasons I don't understand, they let me go. Within 24 hours I booked a plane ticket, found someone to sublet my apartment in exchange for doing some work and errands for me, and left.

That summer the course of my life changed. I ended up co-founding a company called Matternet that was not only successful in its own right, but launched the global commercial drone transport industry. During this experience, every day I felt I was working way beyond my capabilities. I had studied history in college and wasn't trained in engineering or technology. I knew little about business and entrepreneurship, as I had worked with nonprofits most of my career. In fact, I didn't even know what stock or equity was when I co-founded my first company. Yet, while I felt I was in way over my head, I tried the best I could and challenged myself to learn and try something new each day.

At one point, I had a huge breakthrough. When we first started the drone transport company, everyone thought it was a terrible idea and told us so. I was surrounded by some of the world's top technology and business experts, and they insisted the company would never work. But here is the thing—it did work! The company not only succeeded but also helped launch an entire drone transport industry inspiring hundreds of other startups and large companies to work with drones in different ways.

I learned something profound about courage and confidence that summer: no one knows how the future will unfold or what will work or won't work, or who is capable or incapable of doing something. Furthermore, there are often many different pathways for a new idea to succeed. While often experts and people higher up the ranks have experience and knowledge that can be helpful, if you're working on something entirely new, no one can know how it'll turn out. You can only know by trying. During those days I stopped looking to other people to tell me if I was right or wrong, or if I was good enough to succeed. Instead I found my confidence by trying things out and seeing if they worked or not in the real world. That was the only way to know, and the results were indisputable.

Today, I believe I can do anything. If I want to work on nuclear fusion, quantum computing, run for public office, become a doctor, build electric tractors, I know I can do it. I also know it might take several years to transition into a new opportunity, and I might have to make sacrifices along the way, giving up time, energy, money, and other opportunities. And while I might choose not to do something, it's because I would prefer to spend my time and resources differently, not because I doubt myself. Instead, the question is, do I want to do it? And what is the best way to do it? Is it worth doing? The question is not, am I capable of doing it? That's what I mean by finding your courage and confidence. You believe in yourself, and know you can overcome the challenges that might come your way.

All that said, this doesn't mean I don't face challenges or live my life without fears or doubts. I still feel nervous giving public talks even though I have given hundreds of them. I'm still impacted by people who tell me that whatever I'm doing is useless or wrong or stupid (the criticism never stops, no matter how good you get.) However, I have also learned not to let those feelings get me down or stop me. I know the feelings will pass, and I will simply move on to the next thing or instead focus on the good things that are happening. As you embark on your own job search and transition, you will have many highs and lows. At times you will feel extremely courageous and confident, and other times full of self-doubt and fear. The key is to realize that how you feel isn't what matters and is not what is important. What is important is that you keep going until you get to where you want to be. What is important is what you actually do, not what you feel.

Now on a practical level, there are limits regarding what one can accomplish with one's own willpower, courage, and confidence. Our world is not a meritocracy and we live in a world that is unfair. Bosses have a say over their employee's work and salary, whether they're good bosses or bad bosses. Venture capitalists and philanthropists decide who gets funding and who does not, regardless if they know what they are doing. Hiring managers don't always hire the best candidates. Billions of people are impacted by biases and inequality. While there have been improvements over the years, and hopefully someday our world will be a better place, for now, we can't escape these realities. So what can each of us do?

At a high level, this book is about social impact. For those of us who can, if we take jobs with companies solving social and environmental problems, we can help change some of the underlying systems that are unfairly holding other people back. That is a long-term solution.

In the short-term, we can also learn from, support, and take inspiration from role models who are finding ways to break the barriers against all odds. I take great inspiration from Hla Hla Win, the school teacher from Myanmar who succeeded despite facing some of the biggest challenges an innovator can face. Although she was an underrepresented woman with no technology background, a mother with a young child from a low-income, war-torn country, with no innovation ecosystem, she still succeeded. Furthermore, she is not the only one. During my time at Singularity University, I worked with founders who started their first companies while pregnant, founders over the age of 80, founders with disabilities, founders based in refugee camps and war zones, and founders from nearly every geographic, ethnic, racial, religious and economic background. All these founders faced different challenges in their journeys, some more than others, yet what they have in common is they showed up and tried, even if the odds were against them (and many of them succeeded.) That said, everyone's situation is different. One of my goals with this book is to help you find a way forward that takes into account the different challenges in your life and where you are today. We will explore those strategies in our next chapter.

Know Your Strengths and Skills

Another part of finding your courage and confidence is reflecting on your strengths and skills and knowing what you have to offer to employers. If you know what you have to offer, the job search becomes more about finding the right match, rather than wondering all the time if you are good enough or not. You can do this by grounding your job search in your skills and accomplishments. I believe there are two different sets of skills important for impact technology jobs. The first set relates to your expertise. The second set relates to your overall mindset and the way you approach your work, manage yourself, and work with others.

Identifying your Expertise

As you explore different impact technology jobs and careers, you will need to think about how your current expertise might be useful to specific impact technology companies.

Are you a firefighter? Your knowledge can be useful to Fire Tech companies, as well as satellite companies looking to monitor wildfires from above, insurance companies looking for ways to evaluate fire-resistant homes, battery companies looking to store batteries more safely, or even Health Tech companies helping patients who live in smoke-polluted regions. Are you into marketing? Given many impact technology companies are building new products people have never imagined or heard of before, they will need a lot of help in telling their stories and helping people understand what they do. Are you currently working in healthcare? There are tens of thousands of Health Tech startups needing the help of doctors, nurses, and healthcare workers. Do you have a background in farming? Your knowledge could be useful to companies building robotic tractors or new types of fertilizers. Have you worked in food service? You can help companies better understand how to use new technologies to best serve customers. Are you a teacher? Ed Tech companies need teachers to help deliver online classes and design new products.

What if you are trained in technology? There are tens of thousands of jobs open to technologists in impact technology companies. Someone needs to build the satellites to detect forest fires. Someone needs to write the code to help self-driving tractors or electric cars navigate. Someone needs to engineer the cells to create lab-grown fish. If you have a technical background, you're in a great position to find an impact technology job.

Mindset

In addition to having a specific expertise, impact technology companies also care about your mindset. If you're reading this book, you're likely fed up with the systems, culture, and mindset of Industrial Era companies. If hierarchies, competition, bickering, low-trust environments, lack of innovation, and a company's inability to change burns you out, this is good news, because it means you have the same values sought by impact technology companies. Impact technology companies want to hire collaborators, people brimming with new ideas, people willing to step up and own their work, and people who celebrate one another's accomplishments.

In general, impact technology companies are looking for workers who are aligned with the future. Earlier we discussed how during the Industrial Era, companies wanted workers who worked similar to robots. They worked in hierarchical structures and did repetitive, rote work as fast as possible. Bringing creativity or taking initiative to your Industrial Era job was seen as disruptive and disrespectful. Questioning your boss, suggesting a better way to do things, or talking to someone too high up the ranks could get you fired. Employees and teams within Industrial Era companies often would compete with one another. It was a winner-take-all scenario. However, the impact technology companies value a different type of worker with a different set of skills. Let's dive in deeper.

Curiosity, Learning, Flexibility and Change

In the Fourth Industrial Revolution, things change quickly. New technologies are invented daily. This means companies must rapidly adjust to keep up with competitors or embrace new opportunities. This means every employee has to constantly be thinking about where the future is going and learning on the job.

Many impact technology companies offer access to online courses or universities as a job benefit as they know their company's success depends on how quickly employees can learn new skills. Given how fast companies change, workers must also be flexible. In job descriptions, you might see companies are seeking workers who are, "comfortable with ambiguity" or "comfortable working in a startup-like environment."

At an impact technology company you might work on a different team or have a different manager every six months, rather than working on the same team for three years. Previously, companies would undergo five-year strategic planning sessions to determine their future plans. Today, companies often change strategies a few times per year, sometimes even making changes on an experimental basis to see what the next best move might be. While an Industrial Era worker will see such behavior as disorganized and chaotic, an impact technology worker will see such an environment as fluid, efficient, and competitive. It's an opposite mindset.

A Positive Mindset

With learning and flexibility, also comes the need for a positive mindset. With so much change, companies are bound to regularly succeed as well as face significant setbacks. You have to stay positive and patient during times of uncertainty. If you talk to any startup or technology company, almost all of them will have a story about the day the company nearly failed. While it's true that some companies do fail, the ups and downs can also be part of the process of working on a new idea. It's important to be able to keep this in perspective, and having a positive mindset also helps you respond more productively to the challenges that might come your way.

A positive mindset is also essential for working at an impact technology company because impact technology companies are solutions-oriented. Historically, we've often addressed social and environmental problems through advocacy—asking those in power to change what they are doing and treat other people and the planet better. Advocacy often involves pointing out bad behavior, complaining, and taking a negative approach.

Impact technology companies are different. They would rather build a new solution to make a problem irrelevant, rather than wait for someone else to change. An advocate will complain about how fossil fuels are destroying the planet. An impact technology company will create a new type of clean energy. An advocate will call attention to discrimination against women. An impact technology leader will launch her own venture capital company and start investing in female founders. While advocacy has an important role to play, especially when people are just learning about new social and environmental problems, impact technology companies are about ending problems by taking control of them. Given this, they tend to hire positive, solutions-driven people ready to create something new.

Teamwork

Many impact technology companies will also post in their jobs descriptions that they value teamwork and collegiality. This is not just a preference, but something essential for the survival of post-industrial companies. In the Industrial Era, everyone and their bosses knew their role and what they were supposed to do every day. This was in a world of hierarchical management and top-down communication. Today, we live in a world where communication is no longer hierarchical, and it's constant and coming from multiple sources. We also live in a world of remote work. You might report to a manager in a different time zone on the other side of the planet. Your team might be located in five different countries. How does teamwork work, when you are not sitting next to each other or are collaborating asynchronously?

As we move into the future, workers are increasingly responsible for managing themselves and managing their communications with their colleagues and managers. Why, because their managers are not sitting next to them to do it for them. Workers might get high-level guidance from their managers, and their managers might be available to brainstorm and problem-solve with them, but each worker is increasingly responsible for figuring out what to do, prioritizing what is most important, and keeping everyone else up to date on what they're doing. Colleagues are also expected to take the initiative to help one another succeed. The way teams work today is very different from the past and turns the hierarchical management pyramids of the Industrial Era upside down and inside out.

Management

Being a manager today is also different than the Industrial Era. During the Industrial Era, managers told their underlings what to do, how to do it, and were responsible for how their underlings performed. This is no longer true. Managers can't tell their underlings exactly what to do because things are changing too quickly, teams are spread out across geographies and time zones, and there is too much to manage. Instead, they must trust their employees to manage their own work, and serve as teachers and coaches. Managers empower their direct reports to succeed on their own and help them solve challenges when needed. They give them high-level strategic guidance regarding what needs to get done and why it's important, but then they step back. Managers of course still intervene for certain types of problems, for example if someone is breaking the law, putting lives in danger, behaving unethically, bullying others, or not meeting their goals on time, but they largely step back from the daily details.

Many people find management today extremely challenging. Managers are in a position where they're responsible for their team's work but can't directly control it. As you get higher up the management and leadership hierarchy, this feeling only intensifies. You have more and more responsibility, and less and less control. Coming to terms with this paradox is essential for managers to succeed and maintain their sanity.

In the future, we may have companies with leaders, but no managers. While we need leaders to provide strategic direction, make decisions, deal with certain problems and bring experience and wisdom to the workplace, technology is making traditional managers less and less relevant. For example, companies called Decentralized Autonomous Organizations (DAOs) are using software to manage work rather than bosses. Imagine a company where the stakeholders articulate the work and tasks to be completed, and then any person is free to complete the work, logging their work through a blockchain system. Imagine how this might change the structure of companies and organizations.

As we transition out of the Industrial Era, it will be a confusing time. If you're interested in this topic, I recommend you check out, *Changemaker Playbook: The New Physics of Leadership in a World of Explosive Change* by Henry F. De Sio, Jr., *The Next Rules of Work: The Mindset, Skillset and Toolset to Lead Your Organization through Uncertainty* by Gary A. Bolles, and *Exponential Organizations* by Salim Ismael, Michael S. Malone and Yuri Van Geest. Each book discusses the future of work for different types of companies and organizations from a different perspective.

Take a minute to reflect on your expertise and your overall mindset toward work. Does it align with working with an impact technology company? Given we are on the brink of entering the Fourth Industrial Revolution, you can probably see some companies charging ahead and reorganizing themselves for the future, and others trying to claw their way back to the ways of the past and what is familiar to them. Most people I know are confused about what is happening in the workplace right now and what a future company will look like. When I feel overwhelmed by some of these larger questions, I remind myself about the challenges of the Industrial Era, and how we spent centuries exploiting the planet and workers. While the future is uncertain, and change can be stressful, we have the chance right now to rebuild everything in a better way. That is the gift and challenge for those of us living and working at this moment in history.

CHAPTER 10—EMBRACE CHANGE: RISK TAKING NEED NOT BE RECKLESS

There's a myth in Silicon Valley that if you want to succeed, you must risk and sacrifice everything. I often hear people advising founders to put all their expenses on their credit cards and borrow money from friends and family to get their ventures started. In some cases, such founders go on to build billion-dollar companies and have rags-to-riches stories. Many will claim this level of risk and sacrifice is the only way to succeed given limited resources and fierce competition. Perhaps.

There are also founders who risked everything and failed dramatically. The pressure of their journeys led to mental health breakdowns, divorces, and suicides. Some founders felt such pressure to succeed they lied to their investors and are now in jail. While some people thrive under pressure and are comfortable risking everything they have, I believe you can also succeed by going at your own pace and taking risks equal to your level of resilience. I've known many founders who worked on their companies for three or four years as a side project before working on them full-time. Others first worked in careers where they saved a lot of money, and then worked on their ventures. We all come from different backgrounds, have different financial resources, and face different challenges in our lives.

While startups are known for being risky ventures, working at established companies can also be risky. This is especially true given the high amount of disruption happening across all industries. You might take a dream job at a large company and stay there for 30 years, or you might face a layoff six months later when the economy takes a dive or an up-and-coming startup disrupts your large company. I know many capable people with bad luck, who have faced multiple layoffs from large companies over the years.

At the same time, there is also a huge risk to not making career moves at all. If you stay in a stable job that you hate, or which causes you a lot of stress, you may end up with physical and mental health problems. If you stay in a job that underpays you for decades at a time, you may jeopardize your ability to enjoy your life or retire. If you never pursue your dreams, you may live with a constant regret that poisons your happiness and your relationships.

So how does one deal with all these different types of risks? I believe the answer lies in committing to make a change, but coming up with a plan to make that change in a way that aligns with your current ability to handle different types of risk. We'll talk about how to do that in the next chapter.

For now, take a moment to consider where you are in your life and how much risk you are willing and able to take. Are you ready to dive into a new career and handle whatever consequences come your way? Or do you prefer to ease into a new career, making small manageable changes over time? Or perhaps you are not ready or able to make any changes at all, and simply want to learn about different possibilities from afar.

CHAPTER 11—CHOOSE YOUR PATH FORWARD: LEARN, EXPERIMENT OR LEAP

Now that we've talked about courage, confidence and risk, let's explore strategies for launching your impact technology career. In my own career, I've used three different strategies at different times in my life depending on how much risk I felt ready to take: learn, experiment, or leap.

At times when I felt I could take no risks, I've simply focused on learning about new careers and job opportunities. While I was learning, I was also preparing myself to take a risk by building up my confidence and finances, so that I was prepared to make a change when I felt ready.

Other times in my life, when I felt more confident and had a small financial safety net, I would find ways to run small experiments that would give me a deeper sense of exposure to new jobs. These experiments went beyond learning. I was putting some skin in the game and creating some real opportunities and relationships to change my career trajectory.

Other times in my life, I took big risks. I leaped. During these times I had a strong financial safety net, or a high level of confidence that I could recover if necessary. I dove right into a new opportunity, willing to take whatever risk was necessary. Let's dive deeper into each of these strategies: learn, experiment, and leap.

Learn

Sometimes in life you feel so much stress you can barely

think. You're living paycheck-to-paycheck, you've lost a job, or are sinking in debt. You might have children or other people depending on you. On top of that, you might have numerous health problems, be in a bad relationship, or be facing other challenges. While some people escape such situations by taking huge risks and succeeding (they argue they have nothing to lose), you can also create a plan of action and change your circumstances at your own pace.

If you find yourself in a situation where you are barely getting by, your first task is to create a plan to stabilize yourself by taking control of your finances and dealing with any toxic situations that are causing you stress. As you start to get things under control, you can then take some steps to start learning about new possible careers, but without putting pressure on yourself to apply to new jobs or make big changes while you are still trying so hard to hold your existing life together.

Early in my career, I had a job I loved, but the job only allowed me to live paycheck-to-paycheck. Because I liked my job, I thought if I worked hard enough, they'd eventually give me a raise. However, I wasn't aware the organization would never give me a raise because of their own financial challenges.

For several years, I just kept working harder and harder, but no matter how hard I tried, I could not reach my goals. I even had dreams at night where I would fail to accomplish something simple, like walk down a hallway. My shoes would stick to the floor or disintegrate and I couldn't move. I felt completely helpless. As the years went by, my confidence plummeted. I began to think my failure to advance was my own fault. I began to believe no one else would ever hire me because I simply wasn't good enough. On top of that, because my coworkers were in the same situation, we all lived in a collective worldview and culture of feeling stuck and accepting it. But I broke free.

I broke out by keeping my existing job while I built up my financial reserves and confidence. I worked a second job on some weekends building up my savings and investing small amounts into a retirement account, something I knew was important to do

YOUR DREAM JOB IS HERE

at a young age and would make me feel more secure throughout my entire career. At night, I read books about the field I wanted to move into. I got the books at the library, or shamelessly perused snippets of books in the aisles of bookstores. Two friends interested in finance helped me set up a budget and reviewed how I was paying down my college loans. I also connected with people outside my existing circle and job who helped me see how valuable of an asset I would be to any company or organization. This gave me the confidence to consider bigger changes. When an opportunity came up through the network I built, I jumped on it.

If you find yourself similarly stuck, focus on financially and emotionally stabilizing yourself and starting a learning journey exploring future careers. Find small ways to earn additional income and save it or pay down your debt so you don't feel so overwhelmed. Broaden your professional and social circles. As you get a handle on your daily life, then start a learning journey to help you learn more about potential future careers.

If you want to create an impact technology learning journey, there are many free resources at your disposal. While I was stuck crouching in bookstore aisles when the Internet was still nascent, today you can find free articles and information on a number of websites. Some of my favorite sites that include articles about impact technology companies are *Wired*, *Fast Company*, *GeekWire*, *Fierce Biotech*, and The World Food Programme Innovation Accelerator. You can also search for impact technology companies online and read up on them. If you know you're interested in a certain topic, such as Ocean Tech or Fem Tech, research those particular topics. You will be surprised at how much information comes up.

I'm also a huge fan of LinkedIn. I follow the founders of companies to get the latest information about what they are working on, as well as learn about free events and online conferences. When you are using LinkedIn, be sure to follow a wide variety of people to get a full picture of an industry. For example, if I want to learn more about artificial intelligence, I won't just follow the companies I hear about on the nightly news. Instead I will do some searches for how artificial intelligence is being used in different industries such as education, deforestation, aerospace, energy grid management, manufacturing, healthcare, humanitarian assistance and more. I also try to find people to follow from different countries and diverse backgrounds. You never know where the next great idea will come from.

In addition to Internet research, you can also explore Meetups in your city or region. I recently attended a Meetup hosted by an aerospace group and a local law firm on autonomous underwater boats, rovers and drones. As I was walking around the parking lot searching for the Meetup, I ran into a woman looking for another Meetup on women's healthcare happening in the same building. Meetups are informal events organized by community members on professional topics or hobbies. Passionate individuals, startups, investors, law firms, and universities often organize them. A website called Meetup posts public events, as well as Eventbrite or Google, if you do a Google search for Meetups.

If you live in a rural area, you might be able to attend Meetups online. You can also host your own Meetup. Even if only one or two people show up, if they are the right people, they can be valuable professional connections. When I was right out of college, my friends and I would host potluck discussion groups. Once or twice a month we would get friends and friends of friends together for dinner to discuss different topics in which we were interested. One time we had so many people RSVP we had two different groups meeting at two different houses the same night. These informal gatherings are useful as it's often a friend of a friend who might be most helpful in connecting to a new job opportunity.

Another idea for meeting people in your area of interest is to set up a job fair. Talk to your local city hall, college, high school, or local business leaders to see if they are interested. Offer to organize the event and invite speakers and attendees from the places where you want to work.

While many of us grew up with the expectation we would learn all we needed to learn in school, that assumption is no longer accurate. We have to keep finding ways to learn on our own to stay professionally relevant. While some adults go back to school to learn new skills, one of the main ways adults learn new skills is from their peers. When I was working on my startups and needed to learn about aerospace and rocketry, I didn't go back to school. Instead, I went to Meetups and conferences and visited other founders at their startups. I asked people to teach me things, for example how a new technology works, or even a skill such as how to solder. Even in my work today, I am constantly meeting with people and learning from them about their work. I have a physics friend in another country whom I've never met in person, but whom I speak with about once a year. He teaches me about quantum technology and I give him advice about entrepreneurship. I also keep in touch with former colleagues and students as they teach me how the world is changing as they launch their own startups and take new jobs. Peer-to-peer learning is an important way for adults to learn in this day and age.

Take a few minutes to think about what you want to learn in the coming months and brainstorm some ideas to get started. Consider writing down a learning journey composed of different websites, books, people, companies, films and more. Make it something enjoyable and fun. Once you are done, pick a few options and get started.

Experiment

In my entire career, I've only found a job once by sending off a resume in response to a job posting advertisement. All of the other jobs came from what I will call running experiments. Running experiments refers to creating opportunities to work with, or get to know, potential employers in an informal way. Running experiments might involve serving as an advisor to a company, consulting, interning, setting up a collaborative partnership, or volunteering.

Early in my career, I often worked one job to pay the bills, and volunteered or interned with other organizations to get to know them. This volunteer work wasn't only about me networking and convincing an employer to give me a job, it also gave me a chance to see if I wanted to work for them and if I would find their work interesting.

One time I walked into an organization where I wanted to work and asked if they had any job openings. The CEO surprised me by saying they'd lost an employee that day and were hosting a major dinner event that night with some important speakers. She asked if I could volunteer at the event checking people in at the reception. I agreed and after the event ended, the CEO offered me a full-time job complete with benefits starting the next day. During the event, she was able to observe that I showed up on time, was polite and helpful to their guests, and got along with the other staff. On my end, I had a chance to work with my potential employer, listen in on the evening's speeches, and got a free dinner.

There are other ways to run experiments outside of volunteering, which I don't recommend doing unless it's for a very short time, as you are often not paid. Instead, you can serve as a consultant or advisor where you engage in limited but specific work. This work pays less than a full-time job and usually does not include benefits, but you can also set your own hours and control your own schedule. Some people are consultants and advisors for only a few hours a month, while others are working on multiple contracts at the same time.

Before I found my job with Singularity University, I first attended as a student. I had a chance to get to know potential colleagues, learn about the work culture, and decide if the programs they were offering were something I found meaningful.

I've also found jobs by setting up strategic partnerships. For example, I worked at one company that collaborated with other companies on special projects and events. When a job opened at a collaborating company, I was first to learn about it and quickly applied. The other company offered me an interview and job because they had already witnessed my professional abilities. If your company doesn't engage in strategic partnerships, you can also pursue this strategy by reaching out to new customers. For example, perhaps you are an accountant or lawyer. You could reach out to an impact technology company of your choice and see if they need help with their legal issues or accounting. In the process, you will get the chance to know them and learn more about them.

Currently, I am serving as a scout for a number of venture capital companies. In this role I refer potential startups to investors for investment. This is a way for me to stay informed of innovation happening in the industry, while also learning about what a venture capital job entails, and if it's something I might want to do over the long-term.

When you are running experiments, while it is great if you can earn money in the process, what you really want to focus on is exploring new careers and building relationships with potential employers so you will be in a good position to make a change if an opportunity comes up. You want to run experiments when you are already in a somewhat stable position. If you are under extreme financial stress or in a toxic work environment, I'd recommend following our strategy under the learn section of this chapter first.

Leap

Are you willing and ready to take a big risk to find your impact technology job? Perhaps you have a solid financial cushion, no responsibilities, a tough skin, or friends and family who will help if needed. Or perhaps you're confident that if you fail, you can recover. If so, you're ready to leap.

Leaping can entail jumping into a new job with an impact technology company right away, or, starting your own company. If you can find a job at an impact technology company you love at the right salary, go for it. Although many impact technology startups are new, meaning some might fail, it can still be a great move. While hopefully your impact technology company won't fail, even if it does, there is still a lot to gain. You will explore a new professional area of interest, gain new skills and work experience, and meet like-minded colleagues who may become part of your professional network for the rest of your life. Given some impact technology companies pay well, you may come out ahead financially over the long term even if you lose your job after a few years. If you are working for a startup, you will also learn the ins and outs of the startup world, perhaps preparing yourself to launch your own startup down the road.

Launching your own startup also requires risk. While we often hear stories of genius founders who launch their companies from their dorm rooms or garage, it's important to know these founders, even if they appear to have done it alone, usually have a lot of people helping them along the way. This reduces their risk of failure.

Who are these helpers? There is an entire ecosystem of investors, companies, lawyers, banks, mentors, advisors and more, who all exist to help startups. These ecosystems are sometimes referred to as innovation ecosystems. Historically, a strong innovation ecosystem emerged in Silicon Valley, but today, innovation ecosystems exist all over the world. These innovation ecosystems are organic. No one is in charge of them or running them, although they tend to attract entrepreneurial people who go on to support them in different ways.

The different players of entrepreneurial ecosystems, whether they are advisors who introduce founders to investors, lawyers who help founders incorporate their companies, early team members, or late-stage investors, often take equity in a startup in exchange for their contribution. This is because many startups don't have a lot of cash when they get started and equity can become valuable over time. So while it is risky to create your own startup, you are also able to share that risk with other people and institutions in exchange for giving them ownership in your company.

How does this work in practice? Imagine you want to start a

new Ag Tech startup. Your first step is to identify a problem in Ag Tech no one else has solved. Perhaps this problem relates to creating better fertilizers or harvesting crops in ways with less spoilage. Then you need to come up with some possible solutions to the problem. Once you have your problem and your solutions, you need to research what other solutions exist and if customers will pay for your solution. If you think people will pay for your solution, and your solution is better than any other solution out there, you are ready to launch your company. If you need money to launch your company, you will need to borrow it, raise investment, or find a grant.

How do you go about finding financial supporters? You can reach out to investors directly, or you can join an incubator or accelerator. Incubators and accelerators are educational programs and institutions that will help you on your entrepreneurial journey. They might help you develop your idea and a prototype of your solution. They might guide you in developing a business plan and a pitch deck. These documents help you research how many people might buy your solution, and clearly explain it to investors, partners, and potential employees. Incubators and accelerators might also introduce you to mentors, advisors, co-founders, employees, and investors. Some will help you with your financials, incorporation, and other legal needs. Some will also help you create your marketing and sales plans and introduce you to new customers. You can think of incubators and accelerators as institutions that help you navigate the innovation ecosystem. They can be especially helpful to first time founders.

Some of the more well-known accelerators and incubators include Y Combinator, 500 Startups, TechStars, Plug and Play, and Mass Challenge, but there are thousands of incubators and accelerators around the world. The World Food Programme runs an innovation accelerator for founders, many from low-income countries, looking to solve problems related to hunger. The Creative Destruction Lab, based out of the University of Toronto in Canada, supports founders with highly ambitious science-based solutions. Two participants I met at Singularity

University, Einstein Kofi Ntim and Christine Ntim, formed one of the world's first and largest digital accelerators, called Global Startup Ecosystem. Einstein and Christine are both global citizens, having spent their lives living in Ghana, the United Kingdom, Haiti and the United States. In 2015, they launched Global Startup Ecosystem to help innovators located throughout Africa, the Middle East and Latin America learn about startups and entrepreneurship. Opportunity Hub (OHUB) is an entrepreneurship center located in the United States supporting entrepreneurs and innovators with a focus on racial equity. Startup Chile focuses on supporting entrepreneurs in Chile and bringing innovators from around the world to Chile to add to the local ecosystem. A fund called Brilliant Minds supports innovators over the age of 60. Given the many incubators and accelerators in the world, you can research them by geography, topic, stage, services they offer, if they offer investment, and more.

During my career, I've worked with the founders of hundreds of startups that have succeeded and failed. While ideally you want to succeed, even if you take a leap and fail, you will learn something along the way. I believe you can learn just as much founding a startup as you might as going to college (although I believe college offers other benefits you can't get from a startup.) If you launch a startup, you will become an expert in the problem you are trying to solve, as well as gain skills in business, management, communications, legal, finance, marketing, human resources and more. Many founders also speak of how creating a startup is personally transformative. Taking on the responsibility of something massive requires you to grow and rise to the occasion and overcome your own challenges and limits.

While taking this leap brings risk, if you are able to stomach that risk, you will gain much. Most importantly, you might come up with a solution that solves a major social or environmental problem. You might help end hunger, find a new way to educate kids in war zones, or provide medical treatment to someone who might not otherwise get it. Along the way, you might create good jobs for your employees, uplifting their lives and their families for generations to come. Your work will also help grow the impact technology revolution and inspire other founders along the way.

While founding a company can be daunting, there has never been a better time to harness some of the world's new technologies and solve our most challenging social and environmental problems. If you're ready to take a leap, I hope you take it and you leap as far as you can.

CONCLUSION—THERE IS MORE TO COME: THE REVOLUTION IS JUST GETTING STARTED

The most challenging aspect of writing this book is that every topic I write about may be outdated by the time this book is published. The world is changing fast. Some of the companies I mentioned might have gone out of business by the time you read this. New ones I didn't mention may have emerged, becoming household names dominating their industries. I also have not been able to include all of the excellent examples of new impact technology companies that founders are building. At one point I started building a database of impact technology companies, hoping to share some solid numbers with you about how many impact technology companies actually exist. After several weeks of logging companies, I realized if I continued, I would never complete this book, because the impact technology companies were emerging faster than I could track them.

I also struggled with how much certainty I should write about the arrival of the impact technology revolution and how big it is. Will the impact technology revolution create hundreds of thousands of jobs? Millions of jobs? Billions of jobs? No one knows. The impact technology revolution is not a certainty—it's a trend. I can point to the new industries, the companies, the hiring practices, and the jobs. While I believe the impact technology revolution will be significant, and even has the potential to become our next global business paradigm, some companies are still trying to return to the ways of the Industrial Era. It's what they know and what feels safe.

Just as our world today is filled with different types of companies, economies, societies, and political systems, the future will likely be a mix of impact technology companies as well as companies trying to return to the past. One thing I do know, is that the more of us who choose to work with impact technology companies, the more powerful those companies will become, and the better off all of us will be.

I also wrote this book at the dawn of easily accessible artificial intelligence. However I chose to write this book without the help of artificial intelligence to ensure the contents are truly my own, and because I value the process of learning through the disciplined cycle of writing and rewriting. However given this, I found myself constantly wondering if this book might have been better with the help of artificial intelligence? Perhaps this fear of missing out is something all of us are now wondering as we go about our lives in a world where artificial intelligence can make anything infinitely better, and nothing will ever be finished. I apologize in advance for any typos or poorly worded paragraphs that my human brain was not relentless enough to find and fix. Imperfection is human, and we can't let being human hold us back.

As I reflect on my own uncertainties and doubts in writing this book, at a deeper level, I know what I am grappling with is a microcosm of what life is like for all of us as the Industrial Era ends and a new era begins. We live in a world that is changing fast, where information and intelligence is now unlimited, where it's difficult to be certain of anything, and it feels impossible to be good enough and keep up. Yet in facing this uncertainty, I refuse to look away and I refuse to stop moving forward.

While uncertainty and lack of clarity can feel unnerving, fundamentally these feelings signal the future has yet to be built. At this moment in time, everything is possible. Those of us who step forward into this uncertainty will be the ones to shape the future. As someone who has devoted her life to social impact and making the world a better place, I desperately want those of you out there who care about making the world a better place, and solving our world's problems, to get involved with technology, now. This is true even if you don't feel you can, even if you feel your work will be imperfect, and even if you don't feel you are ready. Technology is a very powerful tool, and whoever embraces it will shape the future. We need those who care about others, and our planet, to be shaping the future, regardless of everything else. Now is the time to take action, now is the time to leap.

This book is my leap. I believe this first wave of impact technology companies are already here, and they offer us a real fighting chance to solve our social and environmental challenges while also creating meaningful jobs that uplift the lives of millions, if not billions, of people. I hope you will join me in carrying out this vision, and that we leap together.

ACKNOWLEDGEMENTS

This book is not just a book, but rather a convergence of insights gained from a lifetime of professional and personal experiences. Given that, I have a lot of people to thank not only for their support and encouragement in writing this book, but in cheering me on throughout my life.

I have my family to thank, as well as a lifelong set of friends who have encouraged me every step of the way. Some of these friends reviewed different versions of this book, while others simply encouraged me to write it, or were simply there throughout my social impact journey.

In particular, I wish to thank Elizabeth Bast, Karen Bhatia, Alice Chen, Max Erdstein, Greg Francis, Devin Joshi, Nami Jhaveri, Caron Lee, Azuka Okafo, Olivia Samad, Malini Sekhar, Sharona Shuster, Paula Wichienkuer, and Kritika Yegnashankaran.

I want to thank Ray Kurzweil, Peter Diamandis, and my former colleagues and community at Singularity University for introducing me to the concept of exponential technologies. Similarly, I want to thank Bill Drayton and my former colleagues and community at Ashoka for introducing me to the concept of changemaking. Exponential change and changemaking are two of the most powerful forces that I know of in our universe. Marrying them together has been my professional calling over the last decade, as well as the intellectual foundation for this book. I can't wait to see these two forces continue to intertwine, creating an impact technology revolution that can dramatically change our world for the better.

I wish to thank the early pioneers of the impact technology industry, including some of those featured in this book: Dr. Sanjeev Arora, Lucrezia Bisignani, Muriel Clauson Closs, Dr. Mary

Lou Jepsen, Juan Francisco Llamazares, Dr. Sara Naseri, Abi Ramanan, Paola Santana, Brainy Swaibu, Søren Therkelsen, Mariana Vasconcelos, and Hla Hla Win.

I also wish to thank Angelika Blendstrup, Nichol Bradford, Ignacio Juarez, Dermot Mee, Kris Østergaard, and Vince Pérez, for their encouragement and support. I want to give a special thank you to Henry F. De Sio, Jr., who was the first person who gave me practical advice on writing this book, and who introduced me to Lynn Reeves Griffin, who was a great source of inspiration and clarity when this book was still a nascent idea.

Last but not least, I want to thank you, the future workforce, who will lead and chart the course of the impact technology revolution for decades to come.

ABOUT THE AUTHOR

Darlene Damm

Darlene Damm is an impact-driven visionary who pioneered the impact technology industry. She co-founded two of the world's first impact technology companies in aerospace and drone transport, and as Faculty Chair and Vice President of Community and Impact at Singularity University, taught and mentored thousands of founders and executives who  went on to build impact technology companies in every industry including Ag Tech, Food Tech, Ed Tech, Climate Tech, Gov Tech, Health Tech, and more.

Darlene served in leadership, strategy, operational, and expert roles with Singularity University, Ashoka, the World Bank, nonprofits in Vietnam and Myanmar, and has spoken about impact technology at the United Nations, the World Food Programme, SXSW, Google, Salesforce, Intuit, Walmart, Sony, Aramco, and delivered TedX talks in Vilnius and Budapest. She has written articles for Harvard Business Review, Forbes, the St. Louis Post Dispatch, the OECD Forum, the Qatar Foundation, and others.

A number of news outlets including TechCrunch, Fast Company, Venture Beat, Wired, Popular Science, Aviation Week, NPR, Gigacom, Forbes, MoonandBack, engadget, The Denver Post, Le Monde and 60 Minutes have covered her work in drones, rocketry and Singularity University impact technology projects.

Darlene received her bachelor's degree from Stanford University, her master's degree from Johns Hopkins University's Paul H. Nitze School for Advanced International Studies (SAIS), was a fellow with Japan-US Community Education and Exchange, is an advisor to the United Nations World Food Programme Innovation Accelerator, was a mentor with Google's impact accelerator, a judge for Stanford BASES, and served on the Biden Administration's Working Group on Cross Border Trade. She holds patents in drone technology and Authority Magazine featured her as a social impact hero.

PRAISE

"As both an impact visionary and a start-up entrepreneur, Darlene Damm provides fascinating insights into the new startups solving our biggest social and environmental challenges. Digging deep into her own personal journey, Darlene provides a practical guide on how to get a job in the fast-growing emerging impact technology sectors. *Your Dream Job is Here* is an inspirational roadmap for job seekers and founders alike who want to tackle our world's biggest challenges and succeed in making a positive impact for the greater good. This book is not just for recent graduates, but for workers of all ages and backgrounds who wish to pivot to more meaningful jobs that they enjoy because of a higher purpose – making our world a better place. It took me five career shifts until I found my purposeful mission in life. How I wish I had the benefit of Darlene's book. To the young entrepreneurs I mentor, I would recommend this book as a must read."

-Vincent S Pérez, chairman co-founder of Alternergy, board member of World Wildlife Fund, former Philippine Energy Minister, Wall Street partner, MBA lecturer, and a serial investor in sustainable seafood, eco-tourism and clean energy.

"Forget everything you thought you knew about technology. This groundbreaking book isn't just about the latest gadgets or theories, it's about innovations that are truly changing the world. With captivating real-world examples, Darlene Damm paints a vivid picture of the impact technology revolution, and more importantly, shows exactly how YOU can be a part of it. Whether you're a seasoned professional, just starting out, or need to make a change, this inspiring and practical guide is a must-read for anyone who wants to harness the power of technology for good. This book will leave you feeling empowered and excited about the future."

- Karen Bhatia, Faculty Lecturer of Social Entrepreneurship at Stanford University, Visiting Practitioner at Cornell Tech's Public Interest Tech Program, and former Senior Vice President leading Tech Strategy at the New York City Economic Development Corporation.

"Anyone who is frustrated with the state of the world today must read *Your Dream Job Is Here*. Darlene Damm creates a narrative of hope and optimism based on example after example of brave entrepreneurs meeting market needs, building successful businesses and doing so without destroying the planet. Her capturing of this pivotal point in human history is powerful and poignant. This book is a rallying cry to a generation of workers who recognize the end of the Third Industrial Revolution and celebrate it by creating the Fourth Industrial Revolution. This book is a masterclass in building that new more sustainable and equitable future."

- Dermot Mee, Chief Operating Officer, Singularity University.

"In *Your Dream Job is Here* Darlene Damm provides a thought-provoking blueprint for how the Impact Technology Revolution can give anyone, regardless of background, the opportunity to transition into a more meaningful career with better quality of life and real impact on the world. Read the book and find the job of your dreams!"

-Kris Øestergaard, Bestselling author of *Transforming Legacy Organizations*.

"We must create wealth for all people while considering how our actions impact others and future generations. It's essential to provide wealth, resources, and a healthy environment for everyone to thrive. By doing so, we develop future customers and sustain a world that supports this growth. *Your Dream Job is Here* is a great resource for job seekers and can also help business leaders understand how technology is a game changer, creating a new generation of companies that are good for the world and its people while generating financial value."

- Ignacio Juarez, Entrepreneur in energy infrastructure and former Founder and CEO of Semtive

Made in United States
Troutdale, OR
07/13/2024

21199378R00076